ACADEMIC LANGUAGE NOTEBOOKS
THE LANGUAGE OF MATH

Course Crafters   **Perfection Learning**®

CREATED AND DEVELOPED BY:

Course Crafters, Inc.

3 Washington Square

Haverhill, MA 01830

Phone: 978-372-3446 x228

Fax: 978-372-3660

www.coursecrafters.com

PUBLISHED BY:

Perfection Learning® Corporation

1000 North Second Avenue, P.O. Box 500

Logan, Iowa 51546

Phone: 1-800-831-4190

Fax: 1-800-543-2745

www.perfectionlearning.com

Printed in the United Sates of America

76292 3

ISBN-13: 978-0-7891-7189-4

ISBN-10: 0-7891-7189-9

3 4 5 6 7 HPS 13 12

TABLE OF CONTENTS

TABLE OF CONTENTS

Understand the Main Idea

Objective Tell the values of digits in numbers above 100.

LESSON
1

Learn the Main Idea

MAIN IDEA You can use place value to read and write numbers and to tell the value of digits in numbers.

Practice Applying the Main Idea

Directions Look at the picture and the place value chart above.
Answer the questions below using complete sentences.

1. What digit is in the hundreds place? What is the value of this digit?

   _____

2. What digit is in the tens place? What is the value of this digit?

   _____

3. What digit is in the ones place? What is the value of this digit?

   _____

4. Why is it important to know the value of digits in a number?

   _____

   _____

Learn the Vocabulary

LESSON 2

Objective Use vocabulary words that will help you talk about numbers and place value.

Learn the Words

Word/Phrase	Definition	Example
digit	a symbol that makes up a number	These are all <u>digits</u>: 0, 1, 2, 3, 4, 5, 6, 7, 8, 9.
number	a symbol that is made up of digits; often used for counting	17 and 598 are both <u>numbers</u>.
value	how much a digit is worth in a number	In the number 20, the <u>value</u> of the digit 2 is tens.
place	location of a digit in a number	The digit 4 is in the ones <u>place</u> in the number 14.
place value	the value we give to the place where a digit is in a number	In 345, the <u>place value</u> of the digit 3 is hundreds.

Practice the Words

Directions Follow the directions after each number below.

Thousands	Hundreds	Tens	Ones

1. Put 4,726 into the place value chart above.

2. What is the <u>number</u> you wrote in the place value chart?

   _____

3. What are the <u>digits</u> in the place value chart?

   _____

4. What is the <u>value</u> of the <u>2</u> in the place value chart?

   _____

5. What <u>place</u> is the <u>4</u> in the place value chart?

   _____

6. What does a place value chart tell us? How does a place value chart help us in math? Write complete sentences. Use the vocabulary.

   _____

   _____

   _____

Use More Language

Objective Use standard, expanded, and word forms to read and write about different numbers.

Learn the Language

There are three different ways to read and write numbers.

Standard Form
249

Expanded Form
200 + 40 + 9

Word Form
Two hundred forty nine

What is another way to write 924?

Standard Form
924

Expanded Form

Word Form

Practice the Language

Directions Fill in the missing words or numbers in the chart below. The first one is done for you.

	Standard Form	Expanded Form	Word Form
Example	592	500 + 90 + 2	Five hundred ninety two
1		3,000 + 200 + 10 + 5	
2			One thousand, three hundred fifty two
3		500 + 3	
4	2,954		
5			Fifteen thousand, five hundred thirty one

Solve Math Problems

Objective Identify and tell what numbers mean when they change place value.

Learn to Solve Problems

Problem What is the value of the 2 in each of these numbers? Why is the value different in each number?   2,367 8,927 5,284 1,982

	Think	**Write**
Step 1:	Read the problem. Ask yourself: *What do I have to do?*	1. I need to find the value of 2 in all four numbers. 2. I need to tell why the value of 2 is different in each number.
Step 2:	Use a place value chart to list the values of the digits.	

Thousands	Hundreds	Tens	Ones
2	3	6	7
8	9	2	7
5	2	8	4
1	9	8	2

	Think	**Write**
Step 3:	Explain why the values of the digits are different. Use: *The values are different because* _____ .	The values are different because the 2 digit has a different place value in each number.

Practice Solving Math Problems

Directions Follow the steps above to solve the problems below. Use a separate sheet of paper.

1. What is the value of the digit 6 in the numbers 3,469   694   65,122 and 16?

2. What is the place value of the digit 7 in the numbers 72,493   2,197   700 and 7,855?

3. What is the value of the digit 4 in the numbers 4,386   642 and 364?

4. What is the place value of the digit 2 in the numbers 342   3,421   2,001 and 24,456?

5. Why is the value of the digits different in each number?

Understand the Main Idea

Objective Compare and order whole numbers in two different ways.

Learn the Main Idea

Is tree A taller than tree D?

A 1,432 feet   B 984 feet   C 987 feet   D 1,298 feet

I can compare and order the two trees using either a number line or place value. Now I know that tree A is taller than tree D.

One Way: A Number Line

Tree A, 1432 feet

900 1000 1100 1200 1300 1400 1500

Tree D, 1298 feet

Another Way: Place Value

	Thousands	Hundreds	Tens	Ones
Tree A	1	4	3	2
Tree D	1	2	9	8

MAIN IDEA You can compare and order whole numbers in different ways.

Practice Applying the Main Idea

Directions Use the number line and place value chart below to compare the heights of the trees above. Write 1 next to the tallest tree and 4 next to the shortest tree. Answer the last question on a separate sheet of paper.

1

Tree A, 1432 feet

900 1000 1100 1200 1300 1400 1500

Tree D, 1298 feet

2

	Thousands	Hundreds	Tens	Ones	Order
Tree A	1	4	3	2	1
Tree B					___
Tree C					___
Tree D	1	2	9	8	2

3 Look at questions 1 and 2. Did you order the heights of the trees in the same way? Did you get the same answer using place value and a number line? Why or why not?

Learn the Vocabulary

Objective Use vocabulary words that will help you compare and order whole numbers.

Learn the Words

Word/Phrase	Definition	Example
to compare	when you show how something is the same or different than something else	I can **compare** the piles of beads. There are more beads in the first pile than in the second pile.
to order	when you put things in a line so you can compare them or learn how they are the same or different	250 300 350 400 450 This number line lists the numbers in **order**. The smallest number is on the left; the largest number is on the right.
greater than >	when something is bigger, or taller, than something else	The height of the elephant is **greater than** the height of the mouse. The height of the mouse is **less than** the height of the elephant.
less than <	when something is smaller, or shorter, than something else	
equal to =	when something is the same as something else	The size of the lemon is **equal to** the size of the lime.

Practice the Words

Directions Look at the pictures and then follow the directions. Use a separate sheet of paper.

1. Write a sentence <u>to compare</u> the prices of two of the hats.

2. Put the prices of the hats in <u>order</u> on a number line.

3. Which hat has a price <u>greater than</u> the price of hat C?

4. Which hat has a price <u>less than</u> the price of hat E?

5. Which hats have prices that are <u>equal to</u> each other?

6 · **Compare and Order Whole Numbers**

Understand the Main Idea

Objective Use number lines or rounding rules to round whole numbers.

Learn the Main Idea

I made 88 baskets. About how many baskets did I make?

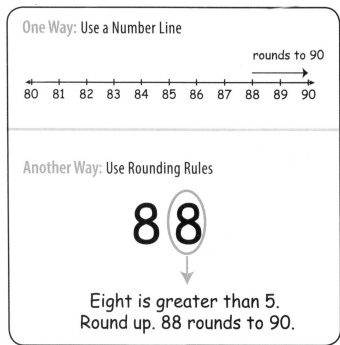

One Way: Use a Number Line

rounds to 90

80 81 82 83 84 85 86 87 88 89 90

Another Way: Use Rounding Rules

8(8)

Eight is greater than 5.
Round up. 88 rounds to 90.

MAIN IDEA You can use number lines or rounding rules to round whole numbers.

Practice Applying the Main Idea

Directions Use both a number line AND rounding rules to round the following numbers. Write your answers on a separate sheet of paper.

1. Round 23 to the nearest ten.

2. Round 74 to the nearest ten.

3. Round 98 to the nearest ten.

4. Round 67 to the nearest hundred.

5. Round 46 to the nearest ten.

6. Look back at questions 1 to 5. Did you get the same answers using a number line and rounding rules? Why or why not?

LESSON 2

Learn the Vocabulary

Objective Write about rounding whole numbers using vocabulary words.

about not the exact number, but close to that number

There are <u>about</u> 280 ants.

---

to round to change a number so it is easier to work with; to find out about how many or much

Example

200   285   300

285 <u>rounds</u> to 300.

---

rounding place the value of the number you round to

Example   Round 687 to the nearest hundred.

rounds to 700

600   687   700

rounding place

The hundreds place is the <u>rounding place</u>.

---

halfway between in the middle of two things or two numbers

Example

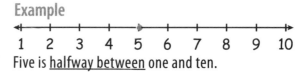

1   2   3   4   5   6   7   8   9   10

Five is <u>halfway between</u> one and ten.

---

increase to go up

Example   The price of the book is now $7.00. It was $6.00. The price <u>increased</u> by $1.00.

Practice the Words

Directions Read the definitions carefully. If the definition is true: (1) write T and (2) write a few sentences that show you know the definition of the word and how to use it correctly. If a definition is false: (1) write F and (2) write why the definition is incorrect. Use a separate sheet of paper.

> Example   **about** a number that is close to an exact answer
> T I'm not sure exactly how many people went to the concert. I think there were about 300 people at the concert.

1. **to round** to replace a number with another number

2. **rounding place** the value of the number you round to

3. **halfway between** at the end of two things or two numbers

4. **increase** to go down or to round down

Use More Language

Objective Ask and answer questions about rounding using *nearer* and *nearest*.

Learn the Language

| How do you round _____ to the nearest _____? | _____ is nearer to _____ than _____, so I round to _____. |

 Practice the Language

Directions Answer each question in a complete sentence. Use a separate sheet of paper.

1. How do you round 2,345 to the nearest hundred?

2. How do you round 768 to the nearest ten?

3. How do I round 6,456 to the nearest thousand?

4. How do you round 752 to the nearest hundred?

Write a question to go with each sentence.

5. 234 is nearer to 230 than 240, so I round 234 to 230.

6. 9,876 is nearer to 10,000 than 9,000, so I round 9,876 to 10,000.

7. 4,567 is nearer to 4,600 than 4,500, so I round 4,567 to 4,600.

8. 1,234 is nearer to 1,230 than 1,240, so I round 1,234 to 1,230.

Solve Math Problems

Objective Identify the correct question to solve rounding problems with *or*.

Learn to Solve Problems

> Problem (Ria was born in 1998.)(Ria's grandfather was born in 1942.)<u>Was her grandfather born about 50 years (or) about 60 years before Ria was born?</u>

	Think	Write/Do
Step 1:	Read the problem and underline the question. The word **or** tells you that the question has two possible answers.	I underlined the question in the problem above.
Step 2:	Circle the facts and decide what to do.	I circled both facts. The problem says "about," so I have to round 1998 and 1942.
Step 3:	A. Round the numbers, and explain how you rounded. B. Write a number sentence using the rounded numbers. Solve the problem. C. Then choose the correct answer from the question.	A. 1998 is closer to 2000 than 1990, so I round to 2000. 1942 is closer to 1940 than 1950, so I round to 1940. B. 2000 − 1940 = 60 Ria's grandfather was born about 60 years before Ria was born. C. So 60 is the correct answer.

Practice Solving Math Problems

Directions Follow steps 1–3 above to solve the word problems below. Remember to explain how you rounded. Solve the problems on a separate sheet of paper.

1. Kunal ate 24 pieces of fruit last week and 33 pieces of fruit this week. Did Kunal eat about 50 pieces of fruit or about 60 pieces of fruit?

2. It is 328 miles from Jonesville to Midtown. Abia drives from Jonesville to Midtown and back. Did Abia drive about 600 miles or about 700 miles?

3. One truck weighs 21,354 pounds. Another truck weighs 28,945 pounds. Do both trucks weigh about 50,000 pounds or about 40,000 pounds?

4. Jae Wan collects comic books. This year he bought 14 comic books. Last year he bought 27 comic books. Did Jae Wan buy about 50 or about 40 comic books?

Understand the Main Idea

Objective Count bills and coins to tell how much something costs and to make change.

Learn the Main Idea

MAIN IDEA You can count coins and bills to tell how much something costs and to make change.

Practice Applying the Main Idea

Directions Read and follow the directions below. Use a separate sheet of paper to show your answers.

Money You Have

Things You Can Buy

1. Count the bills and coins you have. Write a sentence telling the total amount you have.

2. Circle two things you want to buy and write the total cost.

3. Subtract the cost of the two things you want to buy from the money you have.

4. Draw a picture of your change in bills and coins. Write a sentence telling how much money you have left.

Learn the Vocabulary

Objective Talk and write about counting money and making change using vocabulary words.

Learn the Words

bill a piece of paper money

dollar a unit of money that is worth 100 cents

$1 $1 $5

dollar sign ($) a sign or symbol used before a number to show a dollar amount $

decimal point (.) a dot that is used to show where whole dollars end and cents begin $1.25

coin a flat, round piece of money made of metal

cent a unit of money; there are 100 cents in a dollar

cent sign (¢) a sign or symbol used after a number to show cents   ¢

Practice the Words

Directions Follow the directions by each number below.

1 Circle the one dollar bill. Put squares around the coins.

2 Write the ¢ or $ sign next to each number. Then circle any decimal points you see.

____1.23   23____

79____   ____456.78

3 Quarters, dimes, nickels and pennies are all _____.

4 You have a dollar. Your friend wants to trade you one hundred and two cents. Would you trade? Why or why not?

_____

_____

_____

_____

Use More Language

Objective Use regular and irregular past tense verbs to describe how much something cost and how much change you got back.

Learn the Language

I had $2.00. My lunch cost $1.10, I bought milk, a sandwich, and an apple. My change was 90¢.

Today's Lunch

Milk   25 ¢
Juice   25 ¢
Apple   10 ¢
Sandwich   75 ¢

Present Tense Verbs	Past Tense Verbs
actions that happen in the present	*actions that happened in the past*
have →	had
costs →	cost
buy →	bought
is →	was

Practice the Language

Directions Answer each question using a past tense verb from the chart above. Use a separate sheet of paper to complete question five.

> **Example** What did the boy buy?
>
> He bought a sandwich, an apple, and milk.

1 How much did the boy spend?

_____

2 How much did his lunch cost?

_____

3 How much was the boy's change?

_____

4 What coins did the boy have in his change?

_____

5 Pretend that you bought lunch from the menu above. Draw a picture and write three complete sentences to tell what you bought, how much you spent, and what your change was.

Solve Math Problems

Objective Draw pictures to help solve a problem.

Learn to Solve Problems

Problem Marisol had $5.00. She wanted to buy a notebook for $2.50 and a pack of pencils for $1.75. Did she have enough money to buy an eraser for 35¢, too?

Step 1: Read the problem. Underline the question and circle the facts.

Step 2: Draw the bills and coins to show the cost of all the items.

Step 3: Count the money. Ask and answer the question(s) in the problem.

$4.60

The total cost of all three items, $4.60, is less than $5.00. She had enough money to buy the eraser, too.

Practice Solving Math Problems

Directions Follow steps 1–3 above to solve the word problems below. Solve the problem on a separate piece of paper.

1. Jaime had $3.00. He bought a banana for 40¢, juice for 25¢, and a salad for $1.00. How much did he spend? How much was his change?

2. Anna had a five dollar bill, two quarters, and nine pennies. She bought a book about dogs. The book cost $5.30. How much money did Anna have? What was her change?

3. Mike had $10.00. He bought raisins for 35¢, milk for $2.69, bread for $2.50, and eggs for $1.99. How much did he spend all together? What was his change?

4. Lupe had $5.60. She bought an eraser for 35¢ and a pack of pencils for $1.25. Did she have enough money to buy a box of crayons for $2.25?

Understand the Main Idea

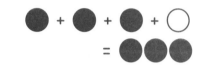

Objective Use addition properties and fact families to solve problems.

Learn the Main Idea

Properties Help You Add

1. Order Property	2. Grouping Property	3. Zero Property
$3 + 4 = 7$ $4 + 3 = 7$	$(5 + 1) + 3 = 5 + (1 + 3)$	$3 + 0 = 3$
You can add numbers in a different order and get the same answer.	You can group numbers in different ways and get the same answer.	When you add zero to a number, you get the same number.

Fact Families Show How Addition and Subtraction Are Similar

$5 + 7 = 12$ $12 - 5 = 7$ $7 + 5 = 12$ $12 - 7 = 5$

MAIN IDEA Properties can help you understand addition. Fact families can help you understand how addition and subtraction are related.

Practice Applying the Main Idea

Directions Write either the name of the property or *fact family* after each number sentence below. Then write a complete *because* sentence to explain why you picked your answer on a separate sheet of paper.

Example	
$3 + 2 = 5$ $2 + 3 = 5$	Order Property This is the Order Property because you can add 3 and 2 in a different order and still get 5.

1 $7 + 0 = 7$

_____

3 $(7 + 7) + (9 + 6) = 7 + (7 + 9) + 6$

_____

2 $9 - 2 = 7$ $9 - 7 = 2$ $7 + 2 = 9$ $2 + 7 = 9$

4 $15 + 9 = 24$ $9 + 15 = 24$

_____

Learn the Vocabulary

Objective Use vocabulary words that will help you understand basic addition and subtraction concepts and how addition and subtraction are related.

Learn the Words

Word/Phrase	Definition	Example
sum	the answer in an addition problem	3 + 2 = 5 5 is the sum
difference	the answer in a subtraction problem	5 − 3 = 2 2 is the difference
addends	numbers that you add in an addition problem	5 + 9 = 14 5 and 9 are addends
fact family	addition and subtraction number sentences that use the same numbers	4 + 3 = 7 7 − 3 = 4 3 + 4 = 7 7 − 4 = 3
inverse operation	number sentences that are opposite of each other, like addition and subtraction	12 + 6 = 18 is the opposite of 18 − 6 = 12. These are inverse operations.
property	a special rule that helps you know how to add; a property of addition is a rule that is always true	Order Property Grouping Property Zero Property

Practice the Words

Directions Match each word or phrase from the first column with the correct example or definition from the second column. Then make sentences that show you know the definition of every word or phrase on a separate sheet of paper.

property ____   **a.** what I get when I <u>subtract</u> numbers

fact family ____   **b.** numbers that you add together

difference ____   **c.** number sentences that use the <u>same</u> numbers

sum ____   **d.** what I get when I <u>add</u> numbers

inverse operations ____ **e.** a special rule that helps you know how to add

addends ____   **f.** Addition and subtraction are _____.

18 • Addition and Subtraction Basic Concepts

© Copyrighted Material – No Reproduction Permitted.

Use More Language

Objective Use similes (with "like") and other clues to define and identify the names of the three addition properties.

Learn the Language

How can I remember the phrase Commutative Property?

Commutative Property is like the word 'commute' which means to go from one place to another place. So 'Commutative Property' means that if the addends are in different places, the sum is still the same.

How can you remember the names of addition properties?

Make a simile using the word "like": _____ is like _____, which means _____. So _____ means that _____.

Practice the Language

Directions Write a simile for each addition property below.

1 Identity/Zero Property

_____

_____

_____

2 Associative/Grouping Property

_____

_____

_____

3 Commutative/Order Property

_____

_____

_____

Answer the following question, using a complete sentence.

4 Why is it important to know about addition properties?

_____

_____

_____

_____

Solve Math Problems

Objective Use drawings or counters to make sure that clue words in word problems really work.

Learn to Solve Problems

Problem Emi gave 10 stickers to Maria and 8 stickers to Tom. She didn't have any stickers |left|. <u>How many stickers did she have before?</u>

	Think	Write
Step 1:	Read the problem. Underline the question. Draw a square around addition or subtraction clue words.	I'll underline the _____. I'll put a square around _____. <u>Left</u> is a _____ clue word.
Step 2:	Read the word problem again. Draw a picture or use counters to draw or show the problem.	I have to find out many stickers Emi had before she gave them away. I _____ subtract.
Step 3:	Ask yourself: *Did the clue word help? Why or why not?*	_____. <u>Left</u> is usually a _____ for subtraction. But in this problem, I have to find the total number of stickers Emi had _____ she gave any away.
Step 4:	Write a number sentence and solve the problem.	10 + 8 = 18. Emi _____.

Practice Solving Math Problems

Directions Follow steps 1–4 above to solve these word problems below on a separate sheet of paper.

1. Juan has a total of 20 stamps in his collection. If he gives his sister 5 stamps, how many will he have?

2. Katya picked flowers for her mother. She picked 5 roses, 2 tulips, and 5 daisies. How many flowers did she pick in all?

3. Sam gave 8 marbles to Ana and 6 marbles to Nelson. Sam had no marbles left. How many marbles did he have when he began playing?

4. Luisa has finished 8 math problems. She has to do 12 problems altogether. How problems does she still have to do?

Understand the Main Idea

Objective Explain what estimation is and when you can use it to add and subtract.

Learn the Main Idea

MAIN IDEA When you estimate, you use numbers that are close to the real numbers, and are easy to add or subtract in your head.

 Practice Applying the Main Idea

Directions Answer the questions. Use a separate sheet of paper if you need to.

1 Which numbers are easy to add in your head? Circle the answer.

   60 + 10   59 + 14

2 Which numbers are easy to subtract in your head? Circle the answer.

   27 − 18   30 − 20

3 Which number sentence is <u>not</u> an estimate? Circle the answer.

   37 + 22 = 59   40 + 20 = 60

4 Which number sentence are estimates? Circle the answer.

   90 − 40 = 50   91 − 42 = 49

5 Look at question 4. How did you know which number sentence was an estimate?

   _____

   _____

   _____

   _____

LESSON
2

Learn the Vocabulary

Objective Talk and write about estimation when adding and subtracting using vocabulary words.

Learn the Words

Directions Write the missing words and numbers on the lines.
Solve the problems and check your answers with your teacher.

exact answer

13 + 29 is exactly 42

An exact answer tells the real sum or difference.

an estimate

13 + 29 is about 40

An estimate tells about how much.

reasonable

40 is a reasonable estimate for 13 + 29

A reasonable estimate is one that makes sense.

Try It On Your Own

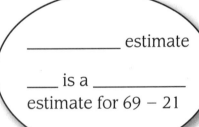

_____ estimate

____ is a _____ estimate for 69 − 21

_____ answer

69 − 21 is exactly ____

_____

69 − 21 is about _____

   Practice the Words

Directions Answer the questions.

1. Circle the problem that shows an exact answer.
   23 + 58 is exactly 81
   23 + 58 is about 80

2. Circle the problem that shows an estimate.
   32 − 18 is exactly 14
   32 − 18 is about 10

3. Circle the reasonable estimate.
   76 − 38 is about 40
   76 − 38 is about 80

4. Write a complete sentence to tell how you solved question 3.

   _____

   _____

   _____

22 • Estimate Addition and Subtraction

Use More Language

Objective Use *because* to explain why you estimated the way you did.

Learn the Language

I used _____ because _____

_____.

Practice the Language

Directions Estimate each sum or difference. Write a sentence.
Tell which estimation strategy you used. Use *because* in the sentence.

1 38 + 43 = ?

_____
_____
_____

3 660 + 169 = ?

_____
_____
_____

2 79 − 65 = ?

_____
_____
_____

4 448 − 252 = ?

_____
_____
_____

Solve Math Problems

Objective Use clue words to decide whether to estimate or find an exact answer.

Learn to Solve Problems

Problem Kiran's basketball team scored 56 points in one game and (approximately) 40 points in the next game. (About) how many points did the team score in all?

Step 1: Read the problem. Underline the question.

Step 2: Circle the clue words. Should you estimate or find an exact answer?
I should estimate.
Explain your answer. I should estimate because the clue words <u>about</u> and <u>approximately</u> tell me I need to estimate.

Step 3: Round the numbers if you need to. Then write and solve a number sentence to show the answer.
60 + 40 = 100

Practice Solving Math Problems

Directions Follow the steps above to solve the problems. Use a separate sheet of paper to write the answers to each step.

1. There are exactly 76 girls and 72 boys in the 3rd grade at Lincoln School. How many children are in 3rd grade at Lincoln School in all?

2. Pedro wants to read 2 books. One book has 112 pages. The other book has 185 pages. He wants to estimate the number of pages he will read. About how many pages do the two books have in all?

3. Cely had about 150 sheets of notebook paper. She used 38 of them. About how many sheets of paper did she have left?

4. On Monday, there were 274 cars in the parking lot. On Tuesday, there were exactly 213 cars in the parking lot. How many more cars were in the parking lot on Monday than on Tuesday?

Understand the Main Idea

Objective Show how to regroup numbers.

Learn the Main Idea

MAIN IDEA Sometimes you have to name numbers in different ways so you can add and subtract them.

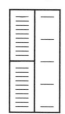 **Practice Applying the Main Idea**

Directions Look at the dashes below. Read each sentence and follow the directions. Draw the new groups on a separate sheet of paper.

1 Add 6 more dashes to the group above. Draw the new group.

2 Add 16 more dashes to the group above. Draw the new group.

3 Subtract 8 dashes from the group on the left. Draw the new group.

4 Subtract 19 dashes from the group on the left. Draw the new group.

5 Why do you sometimes have to name numbers in different ways?

_____

_____

Learn the Vocabulary

Objective Talk and write about addition, subtraction, and regrouping, using the new word and phrases.

Learn the Words

Word/Phrase	Synonym/Definition	Example
to regroup	to **trade**; to exchange amounts of equal value when you rename numbers	I can **regroup** 1 ten and 1 one into 11 ones.
enough	**sufficient**; as many numbers or things as I need	I need 5 stars. I only have 2 stars. I do not have **enough** stickers.

Practice the Words

Directions Choose the correct vocabulary word to complete each paragraph. Answer question 3 on a separate sheet of paper.

1 One group of stars has 1 ten and 8 ones. The other group has 1 ten and 2 ones. I want to add the groups. I have _____ ones to _____ them as 1 ten. Then I have 3 tens. That's 30 stars.

2 There are 30 stars total. I want to subtract 9 stars. I don't have _____ ones to subtract 9. I have to _____ 1 ten as 10 ones. Then I can subtract 9 ones. After I subtract, I have 2 tens and 1 ones. That's 21 stars.

3 Draw two groups of circles. Arrange them in tens and ones. Describe how to add them together. Use the sentences in question 1 as a model. Then describe how to subtract 9 from the total number of circles. Use the sentences in question 2 as a model.

Use More Language

Objective Use sentences with *when* to explain why you need to regroup.

Learn the Language

Explain When to Regroup Using the Following Sentence Frame

When I _____, I need to regroup when _____.

Practice the Language

Directions Read and answer the questions below. Use *when* to explain in a complete sentence why you need to regroup. Use a separate sheet of paper to show your work.

1. Add 38 + 6. Do you need to regroup?

2. How much is 99 + 37? Why do you need to regroup?

3. Add 244 + 189. How do you know you need to regroup?

4. Subtract 35 − 7. Why do you need to regroup?

5. Subtract 268 − 49. How do you know you need to regroup?

Add and Subtract with Regrouping · 27

Solve Math Problems

Objective Write a number sentence in the correct order when you subtract.

Learn to Solve Problems

Problem Lupe had 34 stickers. Yesterday she had 52 stickers, but she gave some to a friend. <u>How many stickers did she give away?</u> (Lupe thinks: *I have to subtract 34 from 52.* 34 − 52 = 22.) What did Lupe do wrong?

Step 1: Read the problem, underline the two questions, and circle what Lupe thinks.

Step 2: Write what Lupe did. She subtracted 34 from 52. 34 − 52 = 22.

Step 3: Identify the total so you can subtract. When I subtract, I begin with the total number. The total is 52.

Step 4: Identify what she did wrong and write the correct number sentence. Solve the problem. Use addition to check. Lupe did not start with the total. She changed the order of the number sentence. The correct order is 52 − 34. I begin with the total number of stickers. I subtract 34 from 52. 52 − 34 = 18.

My answer is 18 stickers. I can use addition to check my answer. 34 + 18 = 52.

Practice Solving Math Problems

Directions Follow steps 1 to 3 on the worksheet to solve the word problems below. Solve the problems on a separate sheet of paper. Explain how you know the order of the number sentence.

1. Franco has 78 baseball cards. He gives 36 to Jose. How many cards does he have left?

2. Monique had 63 buttons yesterday. She gave some to a friend. Today she has 48 buttons. How many buttons did she give away?

3. Amin has to walk 20 blocks to school. He has walked 7 blocks. How many more blocks does he have to walk?

4. Omar has 87 marbles. Yesterday he had 124 marbles, but he gave some to Jun. How many marbles did he give away? Explain how you knew the correct order to write the number sentence.

Understand the Main Idea

Objective Show that multiplying equal groups is the same as adding equal groups.

Learn the Main Idea

You can add four equal groups of cherries: $3 + 3 + 3 + 3 = 12$
You can multiply four equal groups of cherries: $4 \times 3 = 12$

MAIN IDEA Multiplying equal groups gives the same answer as adding equal groups.

Practice Applying the Main Idea

Directions Use the picture to find how many counters there are in all. Then answer the last question on a separate sheet of paper.

1 Add the 5 groups. Write a number sentence. How many counters can you count in all?

_____

2 Multiply the 5 groups of counters. Write a number sentence. How many counters do you have in all?

_____

3 Draw 3 groups with 3 counters in each group. Write an addition number sentence and a multiplication number sentence. How many counters are there in total? Then write a sentence to explain why you can add or multiply.

LESSON 2

Learn the Vocabulary

Objective Define vocabulary words that will help you talk and write about multiplication.

Learn the Words

Word/Phrase	Definition	Picture/Example
equal groups	groups that have the same number of items	array / equal groups
array	a way to show items in rows and columns	
factor	a number that you multiply by another number to get an answer	times product $5 \times 6 = 30$ factors
product	the answer to a multiplication problem	
times	a word that tells you to multiply one number by another number	
repeated addition	adding the same number more than two times	2 + 2 + 2
Commutative or Order Property of Multiplication	You can multiply two factors in any order and get the same product.	3 × 2 = 2 × 3

Practice the Words

Directions Answer questions 1 to 6 with the correct vocabulary word or phrase. Then answer question 7 in a complete sentence on a separate sheet of paper.

1. Circles that are ordered in rows and columns form an _____.

2. Things we can multiply must be in _____.

3. We call the numbers we multiply _____.

4. We call the answer to a multiplication problem the _____.

5. If you add 5 + 5 + 5, you are doing _____.

6. When we add we say *plus,* but when we multiply we say _____.

7. Think about the Commutative or Order Property of Multiplication. Why do we use the word *order* to describe it?

Use More Language

Objective Use *each* to ask and answer questions about equal groups.

Learn the Language

Example

How many rocks does **each** group have?
Each group has 4 rocks.

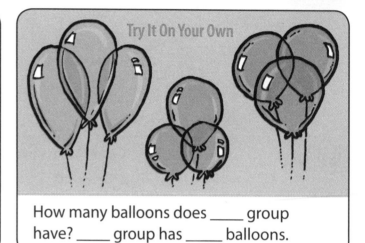

Try It On Your Own

How many balloons does _____ group
have? _____ group has _____ balloons.

Practice the Language

Directions Use the word *each* to ask or answer questions about the arrays below.
Write complete sentences. Answer question 5 on a separate sheet of paper.

1

How many pencils does each group
have?

_____

2

Write a question about the stamps using
the word *each*.

_____

3 Write the answer to the question about
the stamps.

_____

4 Explain in a sentence what the word *each*
tells you when you use multiplication.

_____

5 On a separate sheet of paper, draw
several groups of circles. Draw the same
number of circles in each group. Write
a question about how many circles
each group has. Write the answer to the
question.

Solve Math Problems

Objective Use clue words and equal groups to choose the correct operation.

Learn to Solve Problems

Problem A classroom has 6 rows of student desks. There are 5 student desks in (each) row. What is the (total) number of student desks in the classroom?

	Think	Write
Step 1:	Read the problem. Circle clue words for addition or multiplication.	I see _____ and I see _____. I will circle _____ and _____.
Step 2:	Decide if the groups are equal. If the groups are equal, multiply. If not, add.	Each row means equal groups, so I will _____.
Step 3:	Write the number sentence, and solve it.	I can write a multiplication sentence: _____ I can make an array or count by 5s. $6 \times 5 =$ _____. There are _____ _____.

Practice Solving Math Problems

Directions Follow the steps above to solve problems 1 to 3. Use a separate sheet of paper. Write the answers to questions 4 and 5 on the paper, too.

1. Ashley planted a garden with 6 lettuce plants in one row, 4 tomato plants in another row, and 20 onion plants in another row. How many plants did Ashley plant in all?

2. A pane of stamps has 5 stamps in each row. There are 3 rows on the pane. What is the total number of stamps on the pane?

3. My calculator has 4 keys in each row. There are 5 columns of keys. What is the total number of keys on the calculator?

4. Explain how you knew whether to use addition or multiplication in problem 1.

5. Explain how you knew whether to use addition or multiplication in problem 2.

Understand the Main Idea

Objective Use skip counting and doubling to solve multiplication problems.

Learn the Main Idea

MAIN IDEA There are many different ways to find products.

Practice Applying the Main Idea

Directions Use skip counting or doubling to solve the problems. Show your work on a separate sheet of paper.

1 A juggler has 2 balls.

a. If the juggler skip counts by 2s 6 times, how many balls will she have?

_____

b. If the juggler doubles the number of balls she juggles, how many balls will she have?

_____

c. If the juggler skip counts by 2s 8 times, how many balls will she have?

_____

2 Write a sentence telling which way you like better to find products. Explain why.

_____

_____

_____

Learn the Vocabulary

Objective Use vocabulary words that will help you talk and write about finding multiplication facts.

Learn the Words

Word/Phrase	Definition	Example
breaking apart	when I separate a number into two smaller numbers because the smaller numbers are easier to multiply	⬭⬭⬭⬭ $2 \times 4 = 8$ ⬭⬭⬭⬭ $2 \times 4 = 8$ ⬭⬭⬭⬭ ⬭⬭⬭⬭ $8 + 8 = 16$
doubling/doubles	when I add a number to itself; when both addends in the addition problem are the same, they are doubles	$8 + 8 = 16$ is an example of <u>doubling</u>.
Identity Property of Multiplication	when I multiply a number by 1, the answer is that number	$5 \times 1 = 5$ is an example of the <u>Identity Property of Multiplication</u>.
pattern	numbers or things that follow an order so you can tell what comes next	3, 6, 9. I can tell the next number in the <u>pattern</u> is 12.
skip counting	when I count from one number to another, not counting the numbers in between	When I count 4, 8, 12, 16, I am skip counting by 4s.
Zero Property of Multiplication	when I multiply any number by zero, the answer is always zero	$4 \times 0 = 0$ $0 \times 11 = 0$ $25 \times 0 = 0$ $0 \times 2 = 0$

Practice the Words

Directions Match the example with the vocabulary words and phrases above.

1 $3 \times 3 = 9$

3   6   9

_____

2 $9 \times 0 = 0$

_____

3 $4 \times 1 = 4$

_____

4 5, 10, 15, 20, 25

_____

5 $3 + 3 = 6, 7 + 7 = 14$

_____

6

$1 \times 7 = 7$
 $1 \times 7 = 7$
 $7 + 7 = 14$

_____

Use More Language

Objective Use *because* to explain how using a specific way of doing multiplication made it easier to multiply.

Learn the Language

How many plants should I plant so all the rows have the same number of plants?

I used skip counting by 5s to multiply 5x3 because it was easy to skip count by fives to the number 15.

I used patterns to multiply 5x3 because it was easy to see the pattern where a number ends in 0 or 5: 5, 10, 15.

I used _____ because _____.

Practice the Language

Directions Solve the problems. Choose one way to multiply from the word bank. Then explain why one way is easier than another way.

> breaking apart   doubling   Identity Property of Multiplication
> skip counting   Zero Property of Multiplication

1 $6 \times 2 =$ ____ _____

2 $5 \times 0 =$ ____ _____

3 $5 \times 5 =$ ____ _____

4 $3 \times 1 =$ ____ _____

5 $8 \times 10 =$ ____ _____

Solve Math Problems

Objective Explain how you solved a multiplication problem using the word *because.*

Learn to Solve Problems

Problem You want to buy 4 rows of stickers. Each row costs 5¢. How much money do you need? How do you know?

	Think	Write
Step 1:	Read the problem and underline the questions.	I underlined the question. I'll have to solve the problem and explain why I used a specific strategy.
Step 2:	Circle the facts and decide what to do.	I know that to get the answer, I need to multiply the number of rows of stickers times the cost of each row of stickers.
Step 3:	Write a number sentence to solve the problem.	4 rows of stickers × 5¢ = 20¢
Step 4:	Explain your answer.	I know that I need 20¢ because 5 × 4 is equal to 20.

Practice Solving Math Problems

Directions Solve each problem below using steps 1 to 4 above. Remember that you can use different ways or strategies. Use a separate sheet of paper.

1. Jan scored 2 goals in each of 8 soccer games. How many goals did she score in all? ____ How do you know?

2. Mia feeds her cat three 3 a day. How many times does Mia feed her cat in 4 days? ____ How do you know?

3. Chong buys 7 packs of baseball cards. Each pack has 5 cards in it. How many baseball cards in all? ____ How do you know?

4. Oman's team played in 6 baseball games. During each game, his team scored 1 run. How many runs did they score in all? ____ How do you know?

Understand the Main Idea

Objective Show how to share equally to find the number in each group. Show how to use repeated subtraction to find the number of equal groups.

Learn the Main Idea

I want to share the strawberries equally. How many strawberries do we each get? I can divide 6 strawberries into 3 groups. There are 2 strawberries in each group. 6 ÷ 3 = 2. We each get 2 strawberries.

I want to give each girl 2 strawberries. How many girls get strawberries? I can give 2 strawberries to Keesha, 2 strawberries to Kaitlyn, and 2 strawberries to myself. 6 ÷ 2 = 3. Three girls get strawberries.

MAIN IDEA Dividing is the same as sharing equally or subtracting equal groups.

Practice Applying the Main Idea

Directions Are these examples of sharing equally or repeated subtraction? Write *share equally* or *repeated subtraction* on the lines. Then answer question 5 on a separate sheet of paper.

> **Example**
> The teacher gave one Vocabulary Card at a time to each student until the cards were all gone. share equally

1 I gave 1 box of raisins to each person. Then I did it again, and again, until all the boxes of raisins were gone.

_____

2 I gave 3 boxes of raisins to one person. Then I gave 3 boxes of raisins to another person, and another, until all the boxes of raisins were gone.

_____

3 I subtracted 5 paper clips each time until I had no paper clips left.

_____

4 I put 15 paper clips into 3 equal groups.

_____

5 Why is it important to know how to divide?

Learn the Vocabulary

Objective Use vocabulary words that will help you talk and write about division concepts.

Learn the Words

Word/Phrase	Definition	Example
to separate	to put into different places or different groups	When I divide, I _____ items into equal groups.
to share equally	to put the same number of items in each group	$8 \div 4 = 2$. I have 8 items. I put them in 4 groups. Each group has 2 items. I _____.
repeated subtraction	to subtract the same number of items until there are none left	$8 \div 2 = 4$ _____ 0 1 2 3 4 5 6 7 8 9 10
divided by	the way we read the symbol $\div$	$8 \div 4 = 2$. 8 _____ 4 equals 2.
dividend	the total number of items that is divided by another number	____ $\div 4 = 2$
divisor	the number used to divide the dividend	$8 \div$ ____ $= 2$
quotient	the answer in a division problem	$8 \div 4 =$ ____

Practice the Words

Directions Write the correct vocabulary word or phrase under each example.

1. I had 12 counters and 6 groups. I put 1 counter in each group, and then I put another counter in each group.

   _____

2. I subtracted 2 until I had nothing left: $12 - 2 = 10$; $10 - 2 = 8$; $8 - 2 = 6$; $6 - 2 = 4$; $4 - 2 = 2$; $2 - 2 = 0$.

   _____

3. I had 12 counters. I put 8 in one group and 4 in another group.

   _____

4. $\underline{12} \div 2 = 6$. 12 is the total number that is divided by another number.

   _____

5. $12 \div 2 = \underline{6}$. 6 is the answer in this division number sentence.

   _____

6. $12 \div \underline{2} = 6$. 2 is the number used to divide 12 in this division number sentence.

   _____

Use More Language

Objective Read and write different forms of written division problems correctly.

Learn the Language

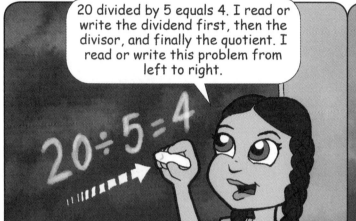

> 20 divided by 5 equals 4. I read or write the dividend first, then the divisor, and finally the quotient. I read or write this problem from left to right.

> 20 divided by 5 equals 4. I read or write the dividend first, then the divisor, and finally the quotient. I have to read or write this problem from right to left and then up.

Practice the Language

Directions Draw lines to match each division problem with the correct word form.

1. $18 \div 3 = 6$

2. $6)\overline{24}$ with quotient 4

3. $6)\overline{12}$ with quotient 2

4. $2)\overline{12}$ with quotient 6

5. $4)\overline{24}$ with quotient 6

a. Twelve divided by two equals six.

b. Twenty-four divided by four equals six.

c. Twelve divided by six equals two.

d. Eighteen divided by three equals six.

e. Twenty-four divided by six equals four.

6. Write these problems in word form.

   $2)\overline{10}$ with quotient 5 $3)\overline{15}$ with quotient 5

   _____

   _____

7. Why is it important to read and write the numbers in a division problem in the correct order?

   _____

   _____

 LESSON 4

Solve Math Problems

Objective Find how many are in each group in a division problem by sharing equally. Find the number of groups by using repeated subtraction.

Learn to Solve Problems

> **Problem** Ned drew 12 pictures of cars. He is going to hang them on the wall in groups of 4. How many groups will he have?

	Learn	Think and Do
Step 1:	Read the problem. Underline the question. Circle the facts. What do you need to find out?	I underlined the question. I circled the facts. I need to find out how many groups of pictures Ned will have.
Step 2:	Decide if this is a division word problem. How do you know? If it is not a division problem, decide what operation to use.	This is a division problem because I know the total. I have to separate the total into equal groups.
Step 3:	Decide how to divide. Share equally if you have to find the number in each group. Use repeated subtraction if you have to find how many groups.	I know that Ned is going to make groups of 4. I have to find out how many groups he will have. I will use repeated subtraction.
Step 4:	Write a number sentence. Solve the problem. Check your answer.	12 − 4 = 8. 8 − 4 = 4. 4 − 4 = 0. I subtracted 3 times. 12 ÷ 4 = 3. Ned will have 3 groups. I can check my answer with counters. I take 12 counters and make 3 equal groups. There are 4 counters in each group.

 Practice Solving Math Problems

Directions Follow steps 1–4 to solve the problems. Using a separate sheet of paper, write the answers to each step.

1. Benny has 16 sticks in equal groups of 8. How many groups does he have?

2. Duong planted 18 flowers in 3 rows. How many flowers are there in each row?

3. Ana has 3 fishbowls. Each bowl has 5 fish in it. How many fish does Ana have?

4. In a complete sentence, tell how you found the answer to question 3.

 © Copyrighted Material – No Reproduction Permitted.

 **40** • Division Concepts

Understand the Main Idea

LESSON

1

Objective Identify the relationship between multiplication and division.

Learn the Main Idea

How many dogs are there altogether? 5 rows of 3 dogs. I can multiply 5 times 3. There are 15 dogs in all!

How many dogs are there in each row? 15 dogs in 5 rows. I can divide 15 by 5. There are 3 dogs in each row!

Multiplication $5 \times 3 = 15$

Division $15 \div 5 = 3$

MAIN IDEA Division is the opposite of multiplication.

Practice Applying the Main Idea

Directions Study the picture of the dogs above. Answer the following questions using complete sentences.

1 How many rows of dogs are there in the first picture? How many dogs are there in a row?

_____

2 How did you find the total number of dogs in the first picture?

_____

3 How many dogs are there in all in the third picture? How many rows are there in the third picture?

_____

4 We know there are 15 dogs in all. How can we find out how many dogs are in each row?

_____

5 How did the two pictures and number sentences help you know that multiplication and division are opposites?

_____

_____

_____

Learn the Vocabulary

Objective Use vocabulary words that help you talk and write about multiplication and division as inverse operations.

Learn the Words

Opposite

Addition	Subtraction
$6 + 5 = 11$	$11 - 6 = 5$

Addition and subtraction are opposite or inverse operations. Subtraction is the opposite of addition.

Multiplication	Division
$6 \times 5 = 30$	$30 \div 6 = 5$

Multiplication and division are opposite or inverse operations. Division is the opposite of multiplication.

Related Facts

3 rows of 7 marbles = 21 marbles
$3 \times 7 = 21$
21 marbles in 3 rows = 7 marbles in each row
$21 \div 3 = 7$

Fact families show all the related facts that use the same numbers. Related facts can help you multiply and divide.

Practice the Words

Directions Fill in the blanks and then answer the questions.

1 _____ is the opposite of division. Multiplication is the _____ of division.

2 What is the relationship between multiplication and division?
_____

3 What are the other three related facts in the fact family $8 \times 2 = 16$?
_____

4 What is unusual about the fact family 5, 5, and 25?
_____

5 Write the number sentences for the fact family above using multiplication and division.
_____

Use More Language

Objective Use *multiplied _____ by* and *divided _____ by* to describe fact families.

Learn the Language

I multiplied _____ by _____ and got _____. I divided _____ by _____ and got _____.

Practice the Language

Directions Write a fact family for each set of numbers. Then describe the fact family in complete sentences using the words *multiplied _____ by* and *divided _____ by*. If you need to, you can use a separate sheet of paper.

> **Example** 2, 3, 6 | 2 × 3 = 6, 3 × 2 = 6, 6 ÷ 3 = 2, 6 ÷ 2 = 3
> First, I multiplied 2 by 3 and got 6. Then I multiplied 3 by 2 and got 6.
> Second, I divided 6 by 2 and got 3. Then I divided 6 by 3 and got 2.

1 2, 7, 14 _____

2 4, 4, 16 _____

3 3, 7, 21 _____

4 6, 8, 48 _____

5 6, 4, 24 _____

Solve Mathematics Problems

Objective Decide whether to multiply or divide.

Learn to Solve Problems

Problem Masumi has a scrapbook with 6 pictures on (each) page. There are 4 pages in the scrapbook. How many pictures does she have in all?

	Think	Write
Step 1:	Circle words that tell you to multiply or divide, like *each, equal number,* and *equal groups.*	I'll need to multiply or divide.
Step 2:	If you <u>know</u> the total, <u>divide</u>. If you <u>don't know</u> the total, <u>multiply</u>.	I don't know the total number of pictures she has. I need to multiply.
Step 3:	Write a number sentence. Solve the problem using a complete sentence.	6 × 4 = 24 Masumi has 24 pictures in all.
Step 4:	Check your answer by drawing a picture.	6 + 6 + 6 + 6 = 24. I solved the problem correctly.

Practice Solving Math Problems

Directions Solve the problems below using steps 1–4 above. Use a separate sheet of paper.

1 Luis invites 20 guests to his birthday party in the park. There are 4 picnic tables. If the same number of people sit at each table, how many picnic tables do they need?

2 Linh wants to know how many cars are in the parking lot. The parking lot has 5 rows of cars. There are 6 cars in each row. How many cars are in the parking lot?

3 Hamid puts 40 sheets of paper into 10 equal piles. How many sheets of paper are in each pile?

4 Marta has 5 sheets of paper. She can fit 4 invitations on each page. How many party invitations can she make if she uses all 4 sheets?

44 • Relation of Multiplication and Division

Understand the Main Idea

Objective Describe different ways to solve division problems.

Learn the Main Idea

MAIN IDEA There are many different ways to find quotients, or answers, to division problems.

Practice Applying the Main Idea

Directions Write three different ways to find the quotient for 8 ÷ 4. Use the pictures.

1.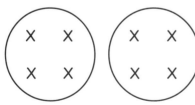

   8 ÷ 4 = 2

   _____

2.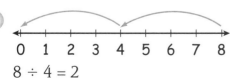

   8 ÷ 4 = 2

   _____

3. $$2 \times 4 = 8,$$
   $$\text{so } 8 \div 4 = 2$$

   _____

4. Choose two of these three ways to find the quotient for 8 ÷ 4. Write a sentence to describe how the ways are alike or how they are different. _____

   _____

   _____

Learn the Vocabulary

Objective Use vocabulary words that will help you talk and write about ways to solve division problems.

Learn the Words

Directions Read the chart. Write the missing words on the lines in the last column.

Word/Phrase	Definition/Example	Word/Phrase in a Sentence
multiplication table	<table><tr><td></td><td>1</td><td>2</td><td>3</td><td>4</td></tr><tr><td>1</td><td>1</td><td>2</td><td>3</td><td>4</td></tr><tr><td>2</td><td>2</td><td>4</td><td>6</td><td>8</td></tr></table>	A _____ is a chart that shows multiplication facts.
repeated subtraction	⌢ ⌢ ⌢ ◄─┼─┼─┼─┼─┼─┼─┼─┼─┼─► 0 1 2 3 4 5 6 7 8 9	When you do _____, you subtract the same number again and again until you reach zero.
division rules	Any number divided by one equals that number. Zero divided by any number equals zero.	_____ tell what happens when you divide with zero and one.

Practice the Words

Directions Look at each picture. Then write the missing words on the line below.

1

	1	2	3	4	5
1	1	2	3	4	5
2	2	4	6	8	10
3	3	6	9	⑫	15
4	4	8	12	16	20
5	5	10	15	20	25

Taylor will use a _____ _____ to find a quotient for 12 ÷ 4.

2

> ### Zero divided by any number equals zero.

Dan will use _____ _____ to find a quotient for 0 ÷ 6.

3

⌢ ⌢
◄─┼─┼─┼─┼─┼─┼─┼─┼─┼─┼─►
0 1 2 3 4 5 6 7 8 9 10

Jasmine will use _____ _____ to find a quotient for 10 ÷ 5.

4 Now choose one of your answers. Write a complete sentence to explain why you chose your answer.

_____

_____

_____

46 • Division Facts

Use More Language

Objective Use *if* to tell about different ways to find quotients.

Learn the Language

Can you use arrays to find a quotient?

28 divided by 4

15 divided by 3

I can use arrays if I can draw rows and columns.

I can use _____ **if** _____.

Practice the Language

Directions Complete the sentences to tell when you can use different ways to divide.

1 I can use equal groups **if** _____
_____
_____.

2 I can use _____ **if** I know how to subtract the same number again and again.

3 I can use _____ **if** I am dividing with 0 or 1.

4 I can use fact families **if** _____
_____
_____.

5 I can find the quotient for 14 ÷ 2 **if** ____
_____
_____
_____.

Solve Math Problems

Objective Write a number sentence to help understand questions in word problems.

Learn to Solve Problems

I'm not sure I understand this problem. I'll write a number sentence to help. I can change some of the words to numbers and symbols.

Three times what number is 24?

I can use '3' for 'three.'
I can use 'x' for 'times.'
I'll use '?' to stand for 'what number.'
I'll use '=' for 'is.'
'24' can stay '24.'

I know that 3 x 8 = 24. So, the answer is 8. Three times 8 is 24.

Three times what number is 24?

3 x ? = 24

Practice Solving Math Problems

Directions Write a number sentence to go with each problem. Then solve each problem. Use a separate sheet of paper.

1. Carmen has a ribbon that is 15 inches long. She cuts it into pieces that are each five inches long. How many pieces does she have?

2. Kyle read 48 pages in a book. He read an equal number of pages each day for eight days. How many pages did he read each day?

3. Olivia collected 25 leaves. She put them into five piles, with the same number of leaves in each pile. How many leaves were there in each pile?

4. There are 28 students in Mr. Soto's class. They sit in groups of four. How many groups are there?

5. Write one or two sentences to explain how you knew what number sentence to use for question 4.

Understand the Main Idea

Objective Demonstrate comprehension of measurement and units of length.

Learn the Main Idea

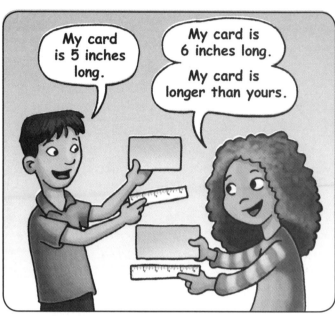

MAIN IDEA We use different units of length to measure how long something is.

Practice Applying the Main Idea

Directions Write *always the same size* or *not always the same size* next to each unit of length. The first one has been done for you. Write number 6 on a separate sheet of paper.

Example — not always the same size

1. 3 1 inch 4 _____

2. _____

3. _____

4. 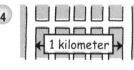 1 kilometer _____

5. _____

6. Why is it usually better to measure with inches than with paper clips? Answer with a complete sentence on a separate sheet of paper.

Learn the Vocabulary

Objective Use vocabulary words that will help you talk and write about length and measuring.

Learn the Words

Word/Phrase	Definition	Example	
to measure	To find how big something is or how much of something there is.	I want **to measure** the length of the bus.	
unit	A unit is a certain quantity that we use to measure things.	I can use these different **units** to measure length.	
standard	A way to measure that never changes and is the same for everyone.	A yard is a **standard** unit of measure.	
customary	Something that we do or we use all the time.	Feet, yards, and inches are the **customary** ways to measure length in the United States.	**Customary Units of Length** 1 foot = 12 inches 1 yard = 3 feet 1 yard = 26 inches
metric	A way of measuring where the meter is the basic unit of measurement.	The boy is 1 meter and 40 centimeters tall in the **metric** system.	1m 40cm

Practice the Words

Directions Fill in the blanks to complete the story. Use the vocabulary words.

Leo wants to <u>measure</u> the length of his new bed. He chooses inches as the _____ of length. Leo knows there are two different _____ systems of measurement. He has just moved to the United States. He wants to learn how to measure using inches, feet, and yards.

He wants to learn the _____ units of length. When he lived in Guatemala, Leo measured things in meters and centimeters. He knows how to use the _____ system very well. Now he wants to learn how to use the _____ system. It will be good to know how to _____ in inches and in centimeters.

Use More Language

Objective Demonstrate the relationships among different customary units of length and different metric units of length.

Learn the Language

Do you use the same unit of measure to measure all these things?

There are 12 inches in 1 foot.

There are 3 _____ in 1 yard.

How many inches are in 1 yard? _____

How many centimeters are in 1 decimeter?

_____

How many meters are in 1 kilometer?

_____

Customary Units	Metric Units
12 inches (in.) = 1 foot (ft)	10 centimeters (cm) = 1 decimeter (dm)
36 inches (in.) = 1 yard (yd)	100 centimeters (cm) = 1 meter (m)
3 feet (ft) = 1 yard (yd)	1,000 meters (m) = 1 kilometer (km)

This table of measures has customary and metric units to measure small and large objects.

 Practice the Language

Directions Which customary or metric unit would you use to measure the length of each object?

1 your foot

_____

2 the distance from one city to another

_____

3 a soccer field

_____

Use a separate sheet of paper to answer these problems:

4 Write these units of length in order from smallest to largest: *yard   inch   mile   foot*

5 Write these units of length in order from smallest to largest: *kilometer   decimeter meter   centimeter*

6 Tell what unit of measure you would use to measure the length of the playground and why. Write a complete sentence.

Solve Math Problems

Objective Choose the correct unit of measurement to describe the length of an object.

Problem Lisa wants to measure her (bedroom). Which (customary) (units of length) could she use?

	Think	**Write**
Step 1:	Read the problem, circle what you have to measure. Circle the unit of measurement.	I will circle <u>bedroom</u>. The problem says <u>customary units</u>, so I will circle that.
Step 2:	Make a list of the units of length in the customary system.	inches, feet, yards, and miles
Step 3:	Think of the size of what you have to measure. Choose the best unit to solve the problem.	A bedroom is too large for inches. The bedroom is too small for miles. I should use feet or yards to solve the problem.

Practice Solving Math Problems

Directions Use the information in the chart to answer the questions.

Object or Distance	Customary Units	Metric Units
piece of paper	1 foot	25 centimeters
baseball bat	1 yard	1 meter
20-minute walk	1 mile	$\frac{1}{2}$ kilometer

1. Ali wants to measure the length of an eraser. Which metric unit of length should he use? _____

2. Jose wants to measure the length of the gym. Which customary unit of length should he use? _____

3. Chung wants to measure how wide a door is. What object can she use?

   _____

4. Kim walks 20 minutes to get from her house to school. About how far does she walk? _____ Her teacher walks half a kilometer from his house to school. About how long does he walk?

   _____

5. How would you measure the length of a baseball field? Choose a unit and a system of measurement. Explain your answer in a complete sentence. Use a separate sheet of paper.

Understand the Main Idea

LESSON
1

Objective Recognize, or know, customary and metric units used to measure how heavy something is or how much something holds.

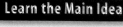
Learn the Main Idea

How much liquid does your bottle hold?

My bottle holds one liter.

My bottle holds one gallon.

How heavy is your box?

My box is five pounds.

My box is three kilograms.

metric   customary   customary   metric

MAIN IDEA You can use customary units or metric units to measure how much something holds, or to measure how heavy something is.

Practice Applying the Main Idea

Directions Look at the pictures above. Answer the questions below. Make sure to use the correct unit of measure. Use complete sentences.

1 How heavy is the girl's box?

_____

2 How heavy is the boy's box?

_____

3 What units of measurement can you use to say how heavy something is?

_____

4 What units of measurement can you use to measure liquids?

_____

Learn the Vocabulary

Objective Use vocabulary words to help you talk about how heavy something is or how much something holds.

Learn the Words

Word	Definition	Example
container	an object, such as a box or bottle, that can hold something inside it	This **container** has milk in it.
to contain	to hold something inside	This box **contains** grapes.
capacity	the amount a container can hold	The **capacity** of this container is 1 gallon.
weight	how heavy something or someone is in the customary system	1 pound — The **weight** of the box of pasta is 1 pound, or 16 ounces.
mass	how heavy something or someone is in the metric system	10 grams — We measure **mass** using grams and kilograms. The grapes have a mass of 10 grams.

Practice the Words

Directions Finish sentences 1 to 4 by telling what you can measure. Then answer question 5 on a separate sheet of paper.

1. When I use a scale, I can measure _____.

2. When I measure using grams and kilograms, I can measure _____.

3. When I talk about what is inside a bottle, I can say the bottle _____ water.

4. When I want to put my milk in something, I can use a _____.

5. List and draw things in your classroom:

   a. 3 things that you can measure to find how heavy they are

   b. 3 things that you can measure to find their capacity

   c. 3 containers you see

Use More Language

LESSON
3

Objective Match equivalent customary or metric units to tell how heavy something is, and how much something holds.

Learn the Language

How much does it hold?

How heavy is it?

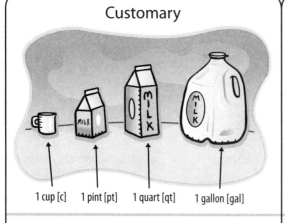

Customary

1 cup [c] 1 pint [pt] 1 quart [qt] 1 gallon [gal]

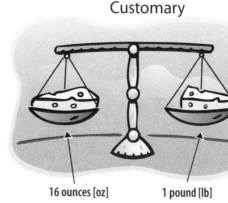

Customary

16 ounces [oz] 1 pound [lb]

Customary
2 cups = 1 pint
4 cups = 1 quart
4 quarts = 1 gallon
16 ounces = 1 pound
Metric
1,000 milliliters = 1 liter
1,000 grams = 1 kilogram

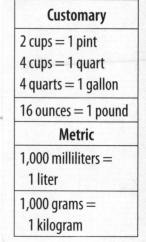

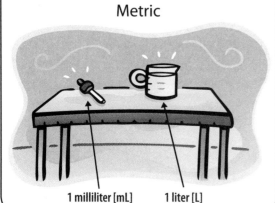

Metric

1 milliliter [mL] 1 liter [L]

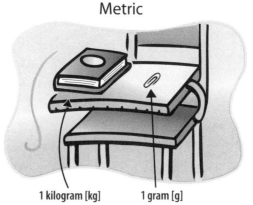

Metric

1 kilogram [kg] 1 gram [g]

Practice the Language

Directions Answer the questions below. Use either the customary system or the metric system.

1 Which container holds more: a pint of milk or a gallon of milk?

_____

2 A loaf of bread weighs 1 pound. What is the weight of the bread in ounces?

_____

3 How many milliliters are there in 2 liters?

_____

4 Which is heavier, 8 grams or 2 kilograms? How do you know?

_____

_____

_____

Solve Math Problems

Objective Choose the appropriate, or best, unit of measurement to solve word problems.

Learn to Solve Problems

Problem
Maria needs 16 cups of juice for the party. Should she buy a quart of juice or a gallon of juice?

Customary Units of Capacity

1 pint	2 cups
1 quart	2 pints
1 gallon	4 quarts

Step 1: Read the problem. Underline the question. What do I have to do?
I have to decide if Maria should buy a quart of juice or a gallon of juice. So I have to find out how many cups there are in a quart and in a gallon.

Step 2: Make a list of units of measurement, from smallest to largest. List how many of the smallest unit there in each larger unit.
cup 1   pint 2   quart 4   gallon 16

> 1 pint = 2 cups. 1 quart = 2 pints, so that's 4 cups. 1 gallon = 4 quarts, so that's 16 cups.

Step 3: Compare the units of measurement. Solve the problem. Write the answer. *A quart is less than 16 cups. A gallon is the same as 16 cups. Maria should buy a gallon of juice because 16 cups equals 1 gallon.*

 ## Practice Solving Math Problems

Directions Read each word problem. Then follow steps 1–3 above. Explain your answer in a complete sentence on a separate sheet of paper.

1. Ani needs to fill her fish tank with 32 cups of water. Should she fill it with 2 gallons of water or 3 pints of water?

2. Gil needs 2,000 milliliters of water for his camping trip. Should he bring a 1-liter bottle or a 2-liter bottle?

3. Min needs 2 pounds of cheese to share with her friends at school. Should she bring 48 ounces or 32 ounces of cheese?

4. A fruit store needs to buy 2,000 grams of apples. Should they buy 1 kilogram or 2 kilograms of apples?

5. What can you measure in both liters and ounces? What can you measure in both grams and pounds?

Understand the Main Idea

Objective Identify what time it is and tell how long something lasts.

Learn the Main Idea

Starting Time: 3:30
Ending Time: 4:00
Homework lasts: 30 minutes
The boy finished his homework after 30 minutes or a half hour.

MAIN IDEA When you know how to tell time, you can find out how long something lasts.

Practice Applying the Main Idea

Directions Write the time shown on each clock. Then tell how long each activity lasts. Write the answer in a complete sentence

1.  Recess
_____
_____ _____ _____

3.  Snack
_____
_____ _____ _____

2. Soccer Practice 5:00 | 5:30
_____ _____
_____

4. Homework 5:30 | 6:30
_____
_____

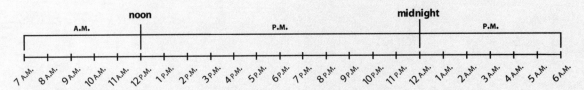

Learn the Vocabulary

LESSON 2

Objective Use vocabulary words that will help you talk and write about time and elapsed time.

Learn the Words

to tell time to find out what time it is on a clock

elapsed time the amount of time between the start and end of an activity

noon · A.M. · P.M. · midnight · P.M.

7 A.M. 8 A.M. 9 A.M. 10 A.M. 11 A.M. 12 P.M. 1 P.M. 2 P.M. 3 P.M. 4 P.M. 5 P.M. 6 P.M. 7 P.M. 8 P.M. 9 P.M. 10 P.M. 11 P.M. 12 A.M. 1 A.M. 2 A.M. 3 A.M. 4 A.M. 5 A.M. 6 A.M.

noon the middle of the day or 12 P.M.

midnight the middle of the night or 12 A.M.

A.M. the time between midnight and noon

P.M. the time between noon and midnight

Practice the Words

Directions Look at the definitions and picture above. Then answer the questions below.

1 What do you do when you tell time?

_____

_____

_____

2 What do you usually do at 2:00 P.M.?

_____

_____

_____

3 What do you usually do at 2:00 A.M.?

_____

4 What time is it when it's noon?

_____

5 What time is it when it's midnight?

_____

6 What does the A.M. and P.M. after times tell us? Why is knowing the difference between A.M. and P.M. important?

_____

_____

_____

_____

7

12:30   **1:30**

Lunch Started   Lunch Ended

What is the **elapsed time** in the two clocks above?

_____

Use More Language

Objective Use *does* and present-tense verbs to ask and answer questions about telling time and elapsed time.

Learn the Language

What time does _____ start?   How long does _____ last?
_____ starts at _____.   _____ lasts _____.

Practice the Language

Directions Look at the classroom schedule to ask or answer the questions. Use complete sentences.

Classroom Schedule

Math	9:00 - 10:00
Social Studies	10:00 - 11:00
Gym	11:00 - 11:30
Lunch/Recess	11:30 - 12:30
Reading	12:30 - 2:00
Language Arts	2:00 - 2:30
Science	2:30 - 3:35

1. What time does science start?

   _____

2. How long does gym last?

   _____

3. Write a question to find out how long math lasts.

   _____

4. Write a question to find out what time reading starts.

   _____

Solve Math Problems

Objective Use clue words to decide when you have to find elapsed time.

Learn to Solve Problems

Azeem's Evening Schedule	
Eat dinner 5:30–6:15	Homework 6:15–7:15
Shower 7:15–8:00	Read 8:00–8:30

Problem Azeem likes to read. He has a schedule he follows so he has time to read every night. (How long) does Azeem (spend) reading each night?

	Think	Write
Step 1:	Read the problem, and underline the question.	I underlined the question.
Step 2:	Circle the clue words. What do you need to do?	The problem asks "how long does Azeem spend reading," so I have to find the elapsed time.
Step 3:	Use pictures or models if necessary. Solve the problem.	The schedule says that Azeem starts reading at 8:00 and finishes at 8:30. I can draw clocks to show the starting and ending times. I look at the 2 clocks and see that there are 30 minutes between 8:00 and 8:30. Azeem spends 30 minutes reading each night.

Practice Solving Math Problems

Directions Read the problem below. Follow the steps above. Write the answer in a complete sentence. Use a separate sheet of paper to draw the clocks and show your work.

1. Max goes to the park at 4:30 P.M. He leaves at 5:15 P.M. How long does he stay at the park?

2. Amit has soccer practice on Tuesdays from 3:30 P.M. until 4:30 P.M. How long does soccer practice last?

3. Marta begins practicing her guitar at 6:00 P.M. She finishes practicing her guitar at 6:20 P.M. How long does her guitar practice take?

4. Wei starts her homework at 6:15 P.M. and finishes it at 7:30 P.M. How long does Wei take to do her homework?

Use More Language

Objective Use *did* and other past tense verbs to ask and answer questions about activities that happened in the past.

Learn the Language

Question	Answer
When did you leave for _____?	I left for _____ on _____.
When did you return from _____?	I returned from _____ on _____.
How long did you stay in _____?	I was in _____ for _____ days.

Practice the Language

Directions Pretend you went on a vacation. On a separate sheet of paper, draw a picture to show where you went. Draw a calendar to show the month you traveled. Circle the day when you left and the day when you returned. Fill in the blanks in the questions with verbs. Then answer the questions in a complete sentence.

1 Where _____ you go on your vacation?

_____

_____

2 When _____ you leave for your vacation?

_____

_____

3 When did you _____ from your vacation?

_____

_____

4 How many days _____ you on vacation?

_____

_____

Write a question about each answer.

5 I left for my grandmother's house on April 1st.

_____

_____

6 I was in Mexico for 15 days.

_____

Solve Math Problems

Objective Use real-world information to solve problems.

Learn to Solve Problems

Problem I started reading a book on October 16th. It took me 1 week and 4 days to read the book. What day did I finish reading the book?

Step 1: Read the word problem and underline the question.

Step 2: Find and circle the facts.

Step 3: Write number sentences. Solve the word problem.

I write 7 for the days in 1 week and add 4 more days to

equal 11. Then I write 16 for the day I started and add 11

days to solve the problem.

7 + 4 = 11 days

16 + 11 = 27

It took me 11 days to read my book. I finished reading my

book on October 27th!

Practice Solving Math Problems

Directions Follow Steps 1–3 above to solve the problems below. Write the answer to each step on a separate sheet of paper.

1. Tam's vacation started on August 8th and ended on August 24th. How many days was she on vacation?

2. My camping trip began on July 5th and lasted for 8 days. When did I return home?

3. It took Mark 3 weeks and 5 days to write a story. He began writing on May 11th. When did he finish his story?

4. Erica started her project on November 15th. She finished her project on November 30th. How many days and weeks did it take Erica to finish her project?

Understand the Main Idea

Objective Use the terms *hot* and *cold* with Fahrenheit and Celsius temperatures on a thermometer.

Learn the Main Idea

You can use temperature to tell how hot or how cold a thing is.
You can measure temperature with a thermometer.

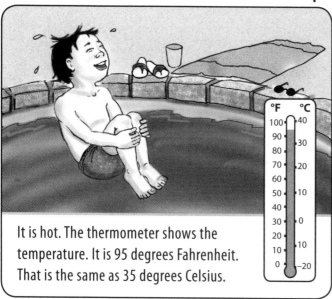

It is hot. The thermometer shows the temperature. It is 95 degrees Fahrenheit. That is the same as 35 degrees Celsius.

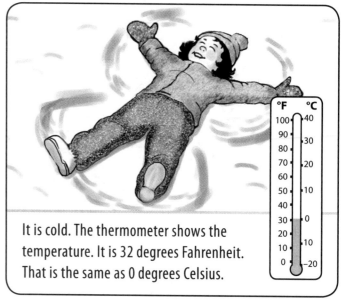

It is cold. The thermometer shows the temperature. It is 32 degrees Fahrenheit. That is the same as 0 degrees Celsius.

MAIN IDEA You can measure temperature with a thermometer.

Practice Applying the Main Idea

Directions Look at the pictures of the thermometers above. Circle the correct answers. Then answer the last question.

1. When the temperature is 95 degrees Fahrenheit, the day is _____.
   hot   cold

2. When the temperature is 0 degrees Celsius, the day is _____.
   hot   cold

3. On a hot day, the thermometer might show _____.
   35 degrees Celsius   0 degrees Celsius

4. On a cold day, the thermometer might show _____.
   95 degrees Fahrenheit
   32 degrees Fahrenheit

5. When is it important to know what the temperature is? Write a complete sentence to answer the question.

   _____

   _____

Learn the Vocabulary

LESSON 2

Objective Use vocabulary words that will help you measure temperature with a thermometer.

Directions Fill in the missing words. Then check your answers with your teacher.

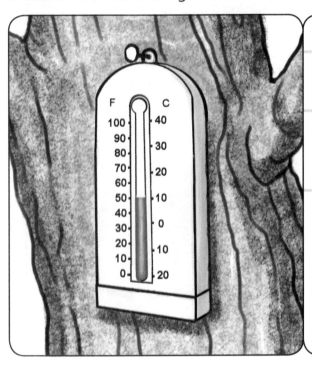

The picture shows a _____.

A thermometer tells how hot or how cold a thing is. It measures the _____.

Every thermometer has a scale. The scale is like a number line. On this thermometer, every mark on the _____ means 10 degrees.

You can measure temperature in different ways. You can use degrees Fahrenheit (°F) or degrees Celsius (°C).

The thermometer in the picture shows 50 _____. This temperature is the same as 10 _____.

Practice the Words

Directions Read the sentences. Fill in the words from the chart so the sentences makes sense.

1. Rey wanted to know how hot it was outside. So, he got a _____.

2. Then he went outside. He held the thermometer up to measure the _____.

3. Rey saw that his thermometer had a _____ on each side.

4. The temperature was 15 degrees on the Celsius scale. That was the same as 59 _____.

5. Now write a sentence that uses the term *degrees Celsius*.

   _____

   _____

   _____

Use More Language

Objective Use different words to describe temperatures.

Learn the Language

Practice the Language

Directions Answer the questions. Use words from the thought bubbles above.

1. Which word is the opposite of *warm*?

_____

2. Which word is the opposite of *cold*?

_____

3. Which word is the opposite of *rise*?

_____

4. Which word means the same as *go up*?

_____

5. Which word means the same as *drop*?

_____

6. Write a sentence that uses the words *rise* and *warm*.

_____

_____

Solve Math Problems

Objective Cross out information you do not need to solve a word problem.

Learn to Solve Problems

Problem Yesterday, the temperature was 77° Fahrenheit. At 8 A.M. today, the temperature was 50° Fahrenheit. Now, the temperature is 72° Fahrenheit. How much has the temperature risen since 8 A.M.?

_____

	Think	Write
Step 1:	Read the problem. Underline the question.	How much has the temperature risen since 8 A.M.?
Step 2:	Circle the facts you need to answer the question.	I need to know the temperature now. I need to know the temperature at 8 A.M.
Step 3:	Draw a line through the facts you don't need.	I do NOT need to know the temperature yesterday.
Step 4:	Write a number sentence. Solve the problem.	50 + ? = 72. I can subtract 72 − 50 = 22. The temperature rose 22 degrees.

Practice Solving Math Problems

Directions Follow Steps 1–4 above to solve the problems.
Use a separate sheet of paper.

1. This morning, the temperature was 40°F. Yesterday morning, it was 45°F. This afternoon, it was 61°F. How much did the temperature rise from this morning to this afternoon?

2. The temperature in David's town is 22°C. The temperature in Hiro's town is 3 degrees cooler than David's town. David likes the temperature at 24°C. What is the temperature in Hiro's town?

3. At 6:00 P.M., the temperature in the park was 60°F. One hour earlier, it was 2 degrees more. The average temperature in the park is 45°F. What was the temperature in the park at 5:00 P.M.?

4. Write a sentence to explain how you know what to cross out in question 3.

Understand the Main Idea

Objective Compare two ways of collecting and organizing data.

Learn the Main Idea

How many people are there in your family?

Six!
Five!
Four!
Nine!
Seven!
Six!
Four!

Number of People in Families

4			
5		
6			
7		
9		

You can make a tally chart or tally table to show this data.

Number of People in Families

```
X        X
X  X  X  X        X
4  5  6  7  8  9
```
Number of People

You can also make a line plot to show this data.

MAIN IDEA When you collect data, you can organize it in different ways.

Practice Applying the Main Idea

Directions Use the pictures, tally chart, and line plot above. Answer the questions in complete sentences on a separate sheet of paper.

1. Look at the pictures of the children. What question did they answer?

2. Look at the pictures of the children. How many children said there were 5 people in their family?

3. Look at the tally chart. How many tally marks are there next to the number 4?

4. Look at the line plot. How many X's are there above the number 8?

5. Look at the tally chart. Look at the line plot. Write a sentence to tell how the tally chart and line plot are alike. Then write a sentence explaining how they are different.

Learn the Vocabulary

Objective Use vocabulary words that help you talk about collecting and organizing data.

Learn the Words

Directions Use the words and the charts to tell how you can collect and organize information. Fill in the blanks.

Step 1:	Think of a question to ask people.	How old are you?
Step 2:	Take a **survey**. Record your **data**.	When you take a _____, you ask lots of people your question. The information you get is called _____.
Step 3:	You can show your data in different ways. A **tally chart** uses tally marks to display data. A **line plot** shows data on a number line.	Ages Number of People: 7 | | , 8 |||| , 9 ||| Ages (line plot): 7, 8, 9 Number of people
Step 4:	Sometimes you can find the **mode** and the **range** of the data.	The _____ is the number in the data that you see most often. The _____ is the difference between the least number and the greatest number.

Practice the Words

Directions Read the sentences and the question. Unscramble the underlined words. Then write each word with the correct spelling.

1. Artur is making a <u>niel lopt</u> to show the information that he collected. _____

2. The difference between the least and greatest numbers is called the <u>engra</u>. _____

3. Marita can make a <u>lylta thrac</u> to show how people answered her question. _____

4. Kiran is taking a <u>yervus</u> to find how many letters people have in their names. _____

5. The <u>omed</u> is the answer that you get the most often. _____

6. How can you use <u>atda</u>? Write a complete sentence about the word. _____

Use More Language

Objective Compare meanings of math words with everyday meanings of the same words.

Learn the Language

Word	Everyday Definition	Math Definition
table	a flat surface with legs, used to put things on 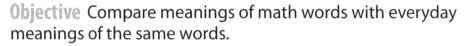	a chart for recording data Ages Number of People: 7 || 8 |||| 9 |||
plot	the action that happens in a story	a chart or a diagram Ages X X X X X X X X X 7 8 9 Number of people
record	to put sound or pictures on a CD, DVD, or cassette tape.	to write down data

Practice the Language

Directions Read the sentences. Look at the underlined words. Circle *everyday* if the word is used in its everyday meaning. Circle *math* if it is used in its math meaning.

1 Julio will <u>record</u> a CD of his band playing their favorite songs.
everyday   math

2 Hannah made a line <u>plot</u> to display the information she got from her survey.
everyday   math

3 How will you <u>record</u> the data you collected yesterday?
everyday   math

4 I thought the book had a very interesting <u>plot</u>.
everyday   math

5 On a separate sheet of paper, write two complete sentences with the word *table*. First, write one sentence for table using the everyday meaning. Next, write one sentence for table using the math meaning.

Solve Math Problems

Objective Answer questions about comparisons.

Learn to Solve Problems

Number of Letters in
Students' Names

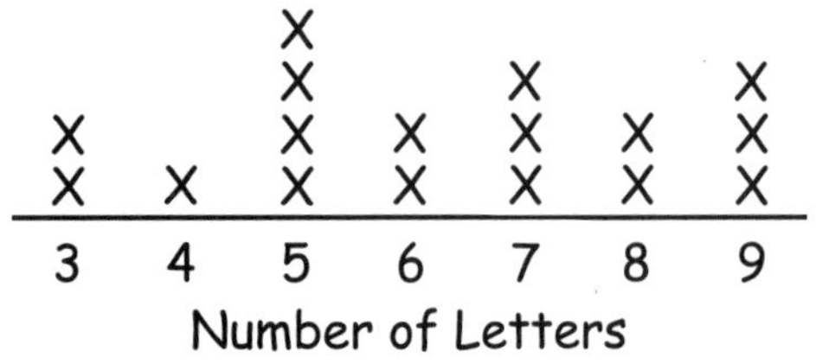

```
          X
          X         X           X
X         X   X   X   X   X
X   X   X   X   X   X   X
3   4   5   6   7   8   9
```
Number of Letters

You can ask and answer questions about line plots and tally tables.

Problem
How many students have names with more than 6 letters?

Answer
I need to look at the names with 7, 8, and 9 letters.

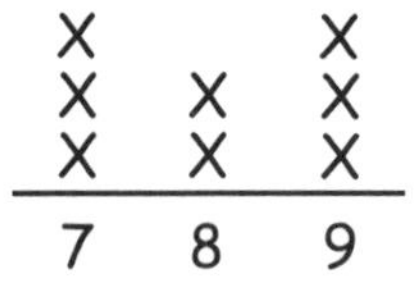

```
X           X
X   X   X
X   X   X
7   8   9
```

3 names have 7 letters.
2 names have 8 letters.
3 names have 9 letters.
3 + 2 + 3 = 8.
So, 8 students have names with more than 6 letters.

Problem
How many more students have names with 5 letters than have names with 4 letters?

Answer
I need to look at the names with 4 and 5 letters.

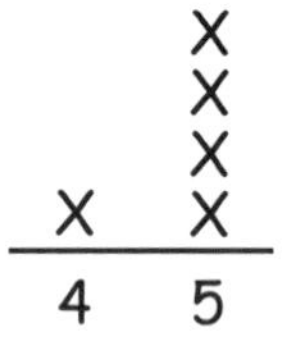

```
    X
    X
    X
X   X
4   5
```

4 names have 5 letters.
1 name has 4 letters.
4 − 1 = 3.
So, 3 more students have names with 5 letters than have names with 4 letters.

Practice Solving Math Problems

Directions Read the questions below, and use the line plot at the top of the page. On a separate sheet of paper, write a sentence to tell what numbers you need to look at. Then write a sentence to answer the questions.

1. How many names have exactly 6 letters?

2. How many names have fewer than 8 letters?

3. How many more names have 9 letters than have 3 letters?

4. How many names have 5 letters or more?

5. Write a question of your own about the line plot. Then answer the question.

Module 19: Data and Graphs

Understand the Main Idea

LESSON **1**

Objective Identify three different kinds of graphs.

Learn the Main Idea

We use graphs to show and compare information.

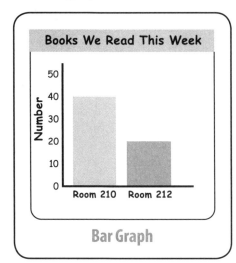

Bar Graph

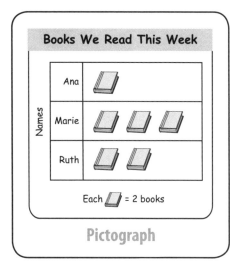

Pictograph

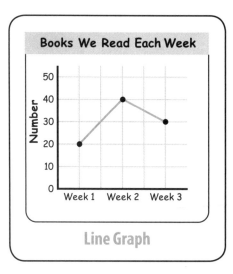

Line Graph

MAIN IDEA Different kinds of graphs show and compare data in different ways.

Practice Applying the Main Idea

Directions Draw lines to match the picture of the graph with the correct name. Then answer the questions.

1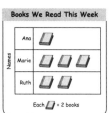

2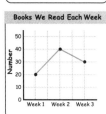

3

line graph

bar graph

pictograph

4 What do graphs do? They _____ and _____ information.

5 Why does it help to show information with a graph?

_____

_____

_____

_____

© Copyrighted Material – No Reproduction Permitted.

Data and Graphs • **73**

Learn the Vocabulary

Objective Use vocabulary words that will help you describe different types of graphs.

Learn the Words

Word	Definition	Example	
graph	a chart or diagram that uses pictures, bars, or lines to show information	This **graph** uses pictures to show information.	Books We Read This Week
title	the name that describes what the graph shows	The **title** of the graph is "Books Read This Week."	Books We Read This Week
label	words that tell what kind of data is in the graph, and how much or how many of each	The **labels** in this graph are the room numbers.	Books We Read Each Week
symbol	a picture that represents data in a pictograph	The book **symbols** in the graph show how many books the girls read.	Books We Read This Week
key	an explanation of what the symbol in a pictograph means, and how much or how many each symbol stands for	The **key** in this graph means that each book symbol equals 2 books.	Books We Read This Week

 Practice the Words

Directions Use the vocabulary words above to complete the story below. Then answer questions 2 to 4 on a separate sheet of paper. Use the data on the graph. Write complete sentences.

Our Favorite Kinds of Books

Picture Books	𝄦 𝄦
Story Books	𝄦 𝄦 𝄦 𝄦 𝄦
Science Books	𝄦 𝄦 𝄦

Key:
Each 𝄦 = 2 students

1. The third-grade students in Miss Jin's class made a _____ to show their favorite kinds of books. The _____ of the graph was **Our Favorite Kinds of Books**. The _____ were the kinds of books. 𝄦 was a _____. The _____ shows that each symbol equals 2 students.

2. What kind of books have the greatest number of votes?

3. What kind of books have the least number of votes?

4. What kind of graph is this? How do you know?

Use More Language

Objective Use comparatives and superlatives to talk about the data you see in graphs.

Learn the Language

Practice the Language

Directions Use the graph below to answer the questions. Write your answers in complete sentences on a separate sheet of paper.

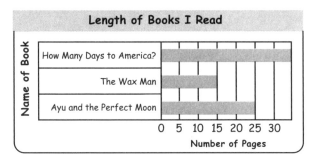

1 Which book is more extensive, *The Wax Man* or *Ayu and the Perfect Moon?*

2 Which book is the most extensive?

3 Write a sentence that compares how short *How Many Days to America?* and *Ayu and the Perfect Moon* are.

4 Write a sentence that compares how short all three books are.

5 If I want to compare how heavy two books are, do I say *heavier* or *more heavy*? Why?

Solve Math Problems

Objective Ask questions using the words *if* and *would,* and tell the result in your answer.

Learn to Solve Problems

Problem

How much did Susana save in June? **If** she had saved $2.00 more, how much **would** she have saved?

Step 1: Read the problem. Underline the questions.
<u>I underlined two questions. I need to answer both</u>
<u>questions.</u>

Step 2: What does the second question mean? <u>What</u>
<u>does "if she had saved $2.00 more" mean? That means</u>
<u>she did not save $2.00 more, but I can imagine she did.</u>

Step 3: Use the graph to answer the first question. Then look at the information in the second question. Use the two numbers to write a number sentence. Solve the number sentence. Answer the second question. Explain your answer.
<u>Susana saved $1.00 in June. $1.00 + $2.00 = $3.00.</u>
<u>She would have saved $3.00. I added the $1.00 she</u>
<u>saved in June and the $2.00 she didn't save. The</u>
<u>answer is how much she would have saved.</u>

Practice Solving Math Problems

Directions Use the bar graph to solve the problems below. On a separate sheet of paper, write the steps you use. Answer in complete sentences. Explain your answers.

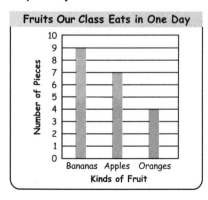

1. How many bananas did the class eat in 1 day? If the class had eaten 9 more bananas, how many would they have eaten all together?

2. How many apples did the class eat in 1 day? If they had eaten 2 more apples, how many would they have eaten in all?

3. Write a problem about oranges. Solve the problem.

Understand the Main Idea

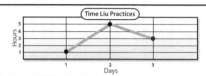

Objective Describe objects using lines and angles.

Learn the Main Idea

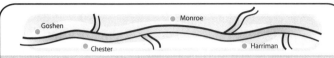

The dots, or points, on the map shows where each town is.

This letter *A* shows two line segments that meet at a point.

This letter *L* shows a corner or an angle. This letter *L* has two line segments.

The dots, or points, on the graph shows how many hours Liu practices every day.

This window shows a corner or an angle.

This road shows a ray. A ray is like a line segment, but it has only one endpoint. The other part goes on without end.

MAIN IDEA We can use points, line segments, and angles to describe objects.

 Practice Applying the Main Idea

Directions Follow the directions in each problem. Draw any pictures on a separate sheet of paper.

1 Circle all the points where line segments meet.

2 Write the letter V. The letter V shows _____ and _____ where they meet.

3 Draw a square window. A square window shows 4 _____

_____

4 Draw a notebook. A notebook shows ___

_____

_____

5 Draw a toy that has line segments that form an angle. Describe the toy using words from this lesson.

_____

_____

_____

Learn the Vocabulary

Objective Write about lines and angles using vocabulary words and phrases.

Learn the Words

This **line** goes in both directions and doesn't end.

These two rays share the same endpoint. The rays make an **angle**.

Degree is the unit we use to measure an angle. We use the ° symbol next to the number in place of the word **degrees**. 45° (45 degrees)

The dot, or circle, shows the **endpoint** of this ray. It can also mark the end of a line segment.

This is a **square corner** and it measures 90°. Right angles are square corners. 90°

Practice the Words

Directions Use the chart above to help you label each picture below. Then describe each picture in a complete sentence.

Example 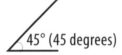 line This line goes in both directions and doesn't end.

1 _____

_____

2 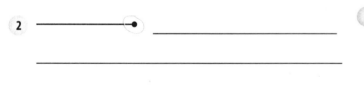 _____

_____

_____

3 75° _____

_____

4 _____

_____

5 Choose two vocabulary words from the chart. Draw a classroom object, like a book, that goes with each word.

_____

_____

_____

Use More Language

Objective Use pictures to ask and answer questions about geometric words.

Learn the Language

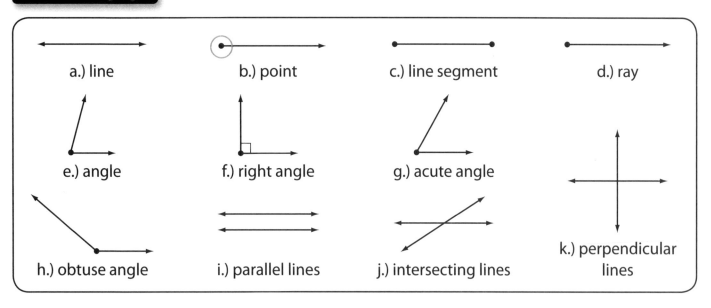

a.) line b.) point c.) line segment d.) ray

e.) angle f.) right angle g.) acute angle

h.) obtuse angle i.) parallel lines j.) intersecting lines k.) perpendicular lines

Practice the Language

Directions Read the question and write the number of the picture that answers the question. Then write a complete sentence.

Example What is a dot that shows where a line segment ends? _b_ _It is a point._

1. What is a part of a line that has only one endpoint? ____

_____

2. What is a part of a line that has two endpoints? ____

_____

3. What are two lines that are the same distance apart and never meet? ____

_____

4. What are lines that cross at the same point but do not form right angles? ____

_____

Now write your own question for each word below. Use the pictures above to help you.

1. acute angle — _____

_____

2. obtuse angle — _____

_____

3. right angle — _____

_____

Solve Math Problems

Objective Explain how geometric figures are alike and different using drawings and definitions.

Learn to Solve Problems

Problem How are (parallel lines) and (perpendicular lines) alike and how are they different?

Step 1: Read the problem. Circle the geometric terms.

Step 2: Look at your Vocabulary Cards and explain what the geometric terms mean. Then draw a picture to show what the problem is about. <u>Parallel lines are lines</u> <u>that are the same distance apart and never touch. Perpendicular lines are lines that</u> <u>cross at a point.</u>

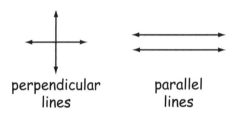

perpendicular   parallel
lines   lines

Step 3: Use *because* to explain how they are alike and how they are different. <u>They are alike because they are both lines. They are different because parallel lines</u> <u>never cross, and perpendicular lines cross.</u>

Practice Solving Math Problems

Directions Follow the steps above to solve the problems below. Write the answer to each step on a separate sheet of paper.

1. How are obtuse angles and acute angles alike and different?

2. How are line segments and rays alike and different?

3. How are intersecting lines and perpendicular lines alike and different?

4. How are lines and line segments different?

Understand the Main Idea

Objective Classify shapes by number of sides and length of sides.

Learn the Main Idea

⚡ 💡 **MAIN IDEA** You can classify shapes in different ways.

✏️ **Practice Applying the Main Idea**

Directions Draw a line to match the correct answer with each question.

1. How are these shapes the same?
   They are the same because . . .

2. How are these shapes different?
   They are different because . . .

□ △

3. How are these shapes the same?
   They are the same because . . .

4. How are these shapes different?
   They are different because . . .

a. one has 3 sides and the other has 4 sides.

b. one has all 4 sides of the same length and the other has some sides of different lengths.

c. they both have 4 sides.

d. they both have sides that are the same length.

5. △ □ □
   △ □ □   Classify these shapes in two groups. Draw a picture to show the groups. Write a complete sentence to tell how you classified them.

Learn the Vocabulary

Objective Use vocabulary words that will help you identify and classify plane figures.

Learn the Words

Word/Phrase	Example	Definition
plane figure	□△○▭	A **plane figure** is a shape that is flat like a piece of paper.
closed figure	□△○▭	A **closed figure** is a plane figure that begins and ends at the same point.
open figure	⌐△◯▭	An **open figure** is a plane figure that is not complete; not all of its sides are connected.
polygon	□△▭	A **polygon** is a closed plane figure with three or more straight sides. A circle is not a polygon because it does not have any straight sides.

Practice the Words

Directions Read the paragraph, and look at the information above. Write the words that go with the pictures.

> Example A plane figure with three sides is a △. <u>triangle</u>

Flat shapes are called □○△. A plane figure that is not complete is an □. A shape that begins and ends at the same point is a ○. A closed figure with three or more sides is a ⬡. You can △ △△ figures by their shapes.

1 _____

2 _____

3 _____

4 _____

5 _____

6 On a separate sheet of paper, write a definition for each word above. Begin each definition: *A ____ is ____.* Use your own words.

Use More Language

Objective Classify polygons to help learn their names.

Learn the Language

Polygons		Triangles		Quadrilaterals	
triangle	△	equilateral triangle	△	rectangle	□
quadrilateral	▭	isosceles triangle	△	square	□
pentagon	⬠	scalene triangle	△	parallelogram	▱
hexagon	⬡	right triangle	◺	rhombus	◇
octagon	⯃	acute triangle	△	trapezoid	⏢
		obtuse triangle	◺		

 Practice the Language

Directions Cover the drawings in the chart at the top of the page. Draw a picture for each figure below.

> **Example**
> an acute triangle △

1. an equilateral triangle

2. an octagon

3. a parallelogram

4. a right triangle

5. Write a definition of a pentagon. Use a complete sentence.

6. Write a definition of a square.

Solve Math Problems

Objective Describe patterns of shapes to decide what comes next in a sequence.

Learn to Solve Problems

Problem

What figure comes next in the pattern?

	Think	Write
Step 1:	Read the problem. Underline the question. Explain what you have to do.	I have to decide what the pattern is. I have to name the next shape.
Step 2:	Name each shape in the pattern. Say the pattern to yourself. Think about how the pattern works.	rectangle, pentagon, pentagon, square, square, square, triangle, triangle, triangle, what? The pattern is 1 rectangle, 2 pentagons, 3 squares, so there have to be 4 triangles.
Step 3:	Choose the shape that comes next. Explain why you chose it. Write a complete sentence to answer the question.	The next shape in the pattern is a triangle because every time there is a new shape, there is one more.

Practice Solving Math Problems

Directions Look at each pattern. Draw the next shape. Write a sentence telling what shape comes next and explaining why you chose that shape.

1 _____

_____

2 _____

_____

3 _____

_____

4 Draw a pattern of your own. Then explain what shapes you used and why it is a pattern.

_____

_____

_____

Understand the Main Idea

Objective Look at shapes to see if they are exactly the same or similar. Fold shapes to see if the two parts match. Move shapes to see if they stay the same.

Learn the Main Idea

These stars are exactly the same size and shape.

I folded the heart down the middle. The two parts match exactly.

These hearts are similar. They are the same shape, but not the same size.

If I move this rectangle to a different place, the rectangle will stay the same.

 MAIN IDEA Some shapes are exactly the same. Some shapes are similar. Some shapes have two parts that match exactly. All shapes stay the same when you move them.

Practice Applying the Main Idea

Directions In questions 1 and 2, name the shapes. Write if the shapes are similar or the same. In questions 3 and 4, write whether the two parts of the folded shapes match.

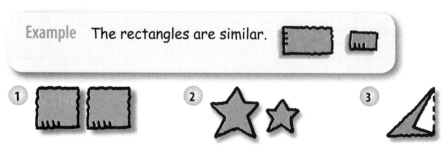

Example   The rectangles are similar.

1 _____

2 _____

3 _____

4 _____

Learn the Vocabulary

Objective Talk and write about how geometric figures are the same or different using new vocabulary words.

Learn the Words

Word/Phrase	Definitions	Pictures/Examples
symmetry	when a figure is folded down the middle so the two parts match exactly	The paper has **symmetry**.
congruent	figures that have the same size and shape	These triangles are **congruent**.
line of symmetry	an imaginary line that goes down the middle of a figure; when you fold the figure on that line, the two parts match exactly	This star has a **line of symmetry**.
symmetric	a figure that has two parts that match exactly	This heart is **symmetric**.
similar	figures that have the same shape; they can be the same size or a different size	The diamonds are **similar**.

 Practice the Words

Directions Write the ending for each sentence on the line. Then on a separate sheet of paper, draw a picture to show the meaning of each sentence.

> **Example** A symmetric figure has <u>two parts that match exactly when you fold it in half</u>.

1 Two congruent figures _____

_____.

3 Similar figures have _____

_____.

2 A figure has symmetry _____

_____.

4 The line of symmetry _____

_____.

Use More Language

Objective Give and respond to commands using *slide*, *turn*, and *flip*.

Learn the Language

How should I move the figure?

Slide the triangle.

Turn the parallelogram.

Flip the star.

Practice the Language

Directions Look at questions 1 and 2. How should you move the figure? Draw an arrow. Look at questions 3 and 4. What do the pictures tell you to do? Use the words *slide*, *flip*, or *turn* to write a sentence.

Example
Turn the triangle.

3 What should I do?

_____

1 Turn the heart.

4 What should I do?

_____

2 Slide the circle.

Solve Math Problems

Objective Ask the questions *Why?* and *Why not?* and explain the answer.

Learn to Solve Problems

Is the Heart Symmetric?

This heart is symetric.

Why?

Because the two parts match exactly.

This heart is not symetric.

Why not?

Because the two parts don't match exactly.

If someone asks you "*Why?*" or "*Why not?*," you have to explain.

Practice Solving Math Problems

Directions Look at each picture. Answer the questions with sentences using *because.*

1. Is this square symmetric?
_____

Why? Why not? _____
_____

2. Are these figures similar?
_____

Why? Why not? _____
_____

3. Does this figure show all the possible lines of symmetry?
_____

Why? Why not? _____
_____

4. Do you think these squares are congruent? _____

Why? Why not? _____
_____

5. Can figures be congruent and similar at the same time? Why? Why not?

_____
_____

Understand the Main Idea

Objective Relate solid figures to the plane figures that form their faces.

Learn the Main Idea

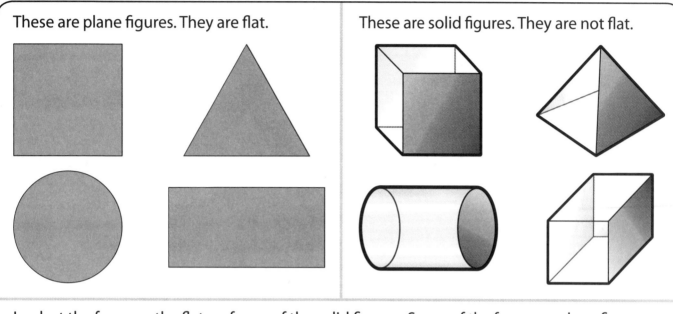

These are plane figures. They are flat.

These are solid figures. They are not flat.

Look at the faces, or the flat surfaces, of the solid figures. Some of the faces are plane figures.

 MAIN IDEA You can describe some solid figures by telling about their parts.

Practice Applying the Main Idea

Directions Read the questions. Look at the solid figures. Circle the correct answers.

1 Which figure has some faces that are rectangles?

2 Which figure has two faces that are circles?

3 Which figure has four faces that are triangles?

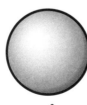

4 Write a sentence that tells about the faces of this solid figure.

_____

_____

_____

_____

Learn the Vocabulary

Objective Use vocabulary words that will help you talk and write about solid figures.

Learn the Words

Directions Fill in the missing words. Then check your answers with your teacher.

A **solid figure** has length, width, and height. An **edge** is the line segment formed where two faces meet.	A **face** is a flat surface of a solid figure. A **vertex** is the point where three or more edges meet on a solid figure. The word **vertices** means more than one vertex.

Example
This solid figure has faces, edges, and vertices.

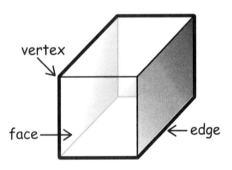

Try It On Your Own
This _____ has faces, edges, and vertices.

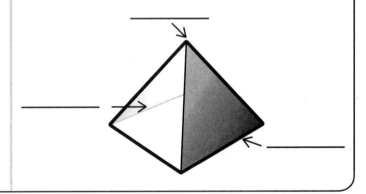

Practice the Words

Directions Use the information above. Write the answers on the lines below.

1. This word describes where two faces of a solid figure meet.

   _____

2. These words describe where three or more edges of a solid figure meet.

   _____ and _____

3. This term tells about a shape that has length, height, and width.

   _____

4. This word describes the flat surface of a solid figure.

   _____

5. Write a sentence to tell how edges and vertices are alike, or a sentence to tell how edges and vertices are different.

   _____

   _____

   _____

   _____

Use More Language

Objective Use the phrase *is shaped like* to connect the names of solid figures with everyday objects.

Learn the Language

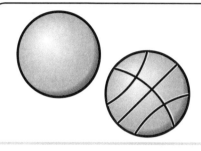

The ball is shaped like a sphere.

The tower is shaped like a cylinder.

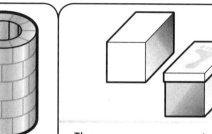

The _____ is shaped like a _____.

The _____ is shaped like a _____.

The block _____ a cube.

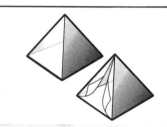

The tent _____ a pyramid.

Practice the Language

Directions Write a sentence to describe each numbered picture. Use the phrase *is shaped like* and one of the words in the box below.

sphere    pyramid    rectangular prism   cube 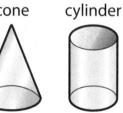   cone   cylinder

1. cereal box

2. orange

3. box of tissues

4. can of beans

_____   _____   _____   _____

_____   _____   _____   _____

Solve Math Problems

Objective Use what you know to solve problems that have unknown words.

Learn to Solve Problems

Problem Hamid puts some (containers) on a shelf. The containers are all the same and are shaped like solid figures. Hamid will be able to (stack) the containers. <u>What solid figures could the containers be?</u>

	Think	Write
Step 1:	Read the problem. Underline the question.	I'll underline the question.
Step 2:	Circle the unknown words. Try to figure out what they mean. Decide if you have to know what they mean in order to solve the problem.	• I don't know what <u>container</u> and <u>stack</u> mean. • A <u>container</u> is something you can put on a shelf. It is shaped like a solid figure. I don't have to know exactly what it is. If I say, "Hamid puts some <u>things</u> on a shelf," I can solve the problem. • <u>Stack</u> is something Hamid can do with the containers. I don't know anything else. Can he stack any containers? I don't know. I can't solve the problem. So I need to ask somebody what <u>stack</u> means or use a dictionary.
Step 3:	Find out what the unknown words mean, if you have to. Solve the problem.	A <u>stack</u> is a pile. <u>To stack</u> means to make a pile. You can stack cubes, or rectangular prisms, or cylinders. So the containers could be cubes, rectangular prisms, or cylinders.

Practice Solving Math Problems

Directions Use the three steps above to solve the problems below.

1. Gisela puts some fish into an aquarium. The aquarium is shaped like a rectangular prism. How many vertices does the aquarium have?

2. Kumari pours water through a funnel. If she cuts the tip off the end of the funnel, what solid figure will the funnel most look like?

3. Yomiri has a jewelry box. The box is shaped like a solid figure. It can slide. Yomiri can open its top. What solid figure could Yomiri's jewelry box be shaped like?

4. Look at problems 1 to 3. Choose a word you did not know. Write one or more sentences to explain how you solved the problem, even though you did not know the word.

Understand the Main Idea

Objective Tell how distance, area, and space are alike and different.

Learn the Main Idea

How can you measure the distance around the square?	How can you measure the area in the rectangle?	How can you measure the space inside the box?
I can measure how far the ant traveled. This tells me the distance around the square.	I can cover the rectangle with squares. I can measure how much area is in the rectangle.	I can fill the box with cubes. I can measure how much space is inside the box.

MAIN IDEA You can measure the distance around a plane figure, the area covered by a plane figure, and the space inside a solid figure.

Practice Applying the Main Idea

Directions Read the sentences and circle or write the correct answers. Then write a complete sentence for number 5.

1. You can measure the **space/distance** an ant travels around a .

2. You can measure the **distance/space** in a ⬜.

3. [grid image] Look at the picture. What do the three shaded squares show?

_____

4. You can measure the space in a 🔲 with **squares/cubes**.

5. Write a sentence to tell how you would measure the distance around a soccer field.

_____

_____

Learn the Vocabulary

Objective Talk and write about distance, area, and space using vocabulary words.

Learn the Words

Directions Write the missing words on the lines.

How can you measure the distance around the square?	How can you measure the area in the rectangle?	How can you measure the space inside the box?
	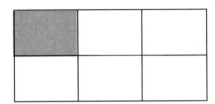	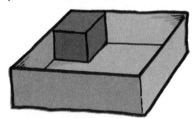
Perimeter measures the distance around a plane figure. Use **units** to measure _____.	**Area** measures how much area a plane figure covers. Use **square units** to measure _____.	**Volume** measures how much space is inside a solid figure. Use **cubic units** to measure _____.
one unit	one square unit	one cubic unit

Practice the Words

Directions Write the missing words on the lines in questions 1 to 3. For question 4, write two complete sentences explaining the picture on the left.

1   I need to find the _____ of this figure. I will measure the area in _____.

2   I need to find the _____ of this figure. I will measure the perimeter in _____.

3   I need to find the _____ of this figure. I will measure the volume in _____.

4   _____ _____

_____ _____

Use More Language

Objective Use *should* to answer questions about perimeter, area, and volume.

Learn the Language

I want to fill the box with potting soil so I can plant a flower. How much soil should I buy?

4 layers x 8 cubic inches per layer = 32 cubic inches

You should buy 32 cubic inches of soil to fill the box.

You should buy _____ of _____ to _____ the _____.

Practice the Language

Directions Write a number sentence to solve the problem. Then write a sentence with *should* to tell how much material you need to buy.

1

3 feet in height

4 feet in length

I want to cover this bulletin board with cloth. How much cloth should I buy?

_____

_____

_____

_____

2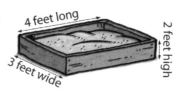

4 feet long

3 feet wide

2 feet high

I want to fill this sandbox with sand. How much sand should I buy?

_____

_____

_____

_____

3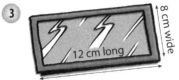

8 cm wide

12 cm long

I want to put a ribbon around this picture frame. How much ribbon should I buy?

_____

_____

_____

_____

Solve Math Problems

Objective Take long questions apart to understand them better.

Learn to Solve Problems

Problem Use cubes to estimate the volume of a cylinder. Will the number of cubes you use be greater than the cylinder's actual volume or less than the cylinder's actual volume?

This is a very long question. I'll try to take it apart.

	Think	**Write**
Step 1:	Read the problem. Underline the question.	I'll find the question and underline it.
Step 2:	Circle the parts of the question that are important.	There are three parts that look important. I'll circle each one.
Step 3:	Think about what each part of the question means.	The first part means "How many cubes do I need to put into the cylinder to estimate the volume?" The other two parts compare the real volume of the cylinder to the estimate with cubes. The estimate could be too much or too little.
Step 4:	Answer the question and explain your answer.	The estimate will be less than the actual volume. The reason is that there will be space left over in the cylinder when you can't fit any more cubes inside.

 ## Practice Solving Math Problems

Directions Follow Steps 1 to 3 above to solve each problem below.
For question 4, write a complete sentence to explain how you solved
one of the problems. Write your answers on a separate sheet of paper.

1. How many 1-inch square tiles are needed to tile a surface that is 6 inches long and 5 inches wide?

2. Jairo built a rectangular prism with 7 layers of cubes and 4 cubes in each layer. What is the volume of the prism?

3. Adrian walks around a swimming pool. If the pool is 20 yards long and half as wide as it is long, how far will he walk?

4. Write a sentence to tell how you solved the problem in question 1 or question 2.

Understand the Main Idea

Objective Tell what a fraction is and why it is important.

Learn the Main Idea

Example 1: Parts of a Whole

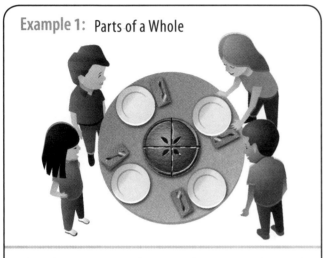

The children are sharing the pie with each other. Each child will have one piece of the pie. Each child will have a fraction of the pie.

Example 2: Parts of a Group

Two cats have spots. One cat does not have spots. A fraction of the cats have spots, and a fraction of the cats do not have spots.

MAIN IDEA A fraction is a number that names a part of a whole or a part of a group.

Practice Applying the Main Idea

Directions Look at the picture of the cats above. Answer the questions.

1. How many cats have spots?

   _____

2. How many total cats are there (including cats with and without spots)?

   _____

3. Fill in the fraction:

   $$\frac{\text{cats with spots} \rightarrow \underline{\quad\quad}}{\text{total cats} \quad\rightarrow}$$

4. Which fraction of the cats have spots? Circle the answer.

   $2 \qquad \frac{1}{3} \qquad 3 \qquad \frac{2}{3} \qquad \frac{3}{4}$

5. Why are fractions important?

   _____

   _____

   _____

Learn the Vocabulary

Objective Use vocabulary words to help you talk and write about fractions.

Learn the Words

Directions Fill in the missing words and numbers. Then check your answers with your teacher.

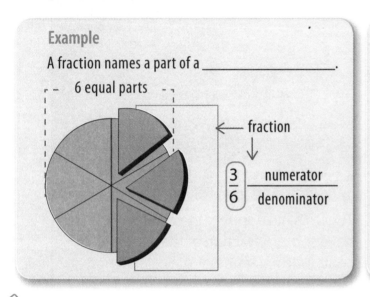

Example

A fraction names a part of a _____.

6 equal parts

fraction

$\dfrac{3}{6}$ numerator / denominator

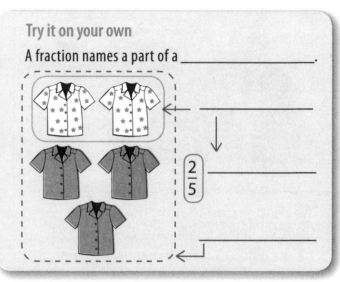

Try it on your own

A fraction names a part of a _____.

_____

$\dfrac{2}{5}$ _____

_____

Practice the Words

Directions Match a question with the correct definition. Write the correct letter on each line.

A What is a fraction?

B What is a numerator?

C What is a denominator?

D What are equal parts?

E What is a group?

F What is a whole?

____ **1** pieces of a whole that are all the same size

____ **2** the bottom part of a fraction; it shows the total number of parts

____ **3** a number of things that go together

_A_ **4** a number that can describe a part of a whole or a part of a group or set of things

____ **5** all of a thing

____ **6** the top part of a fraction; it shows the number of parts you are counting

Now answer each question in your own words using a complete sentence on a separate sheet of paper.

Use More Language

Objective Ask and answer questions about fractions.

Learn the Language

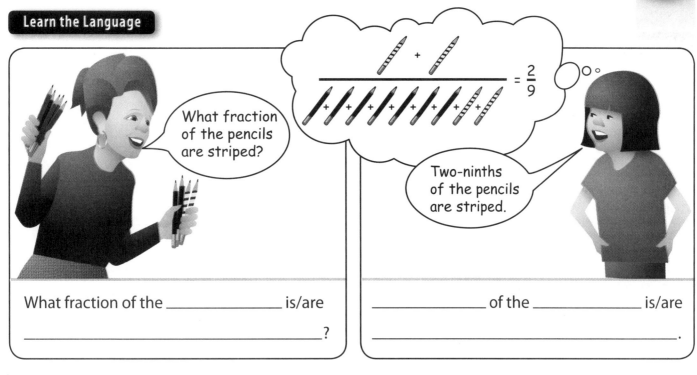

$$\frac{/ \;\; + \;\; /}{/ \;+\; / \;+\; / \;+\; / \;+\; / \;+\; / \;+\; / \;+\; / \;+\; /} = \frac{2}{9}$$

What fraction of the pencils are striped?

Two-ninths of the pencils are striped.

What fraction of the _____ is/are

_____ ?

_____ of the _____ is/are

_____ .

Practice the Language

Directions Look at the picture of the monsters. Answer each question in a complete sentence. Use a separate sheet of paper if you need to.

Example

What fraction of the monsters are blue?

One-fifth of the monsters are blue.

1 What fraction of the monsters are short?

_____

2 What fraction of the monsters have ears?

_____

Write a question to go with each sentence.

1 Four-fifths of the monsters have teeth.

_____

2 Three-fifths of the monsters are tall.

_____

Solve Math Problems

Objective Draw pictures of fractions to help you solve math problems.

Learn to Solve Problems

Problem Manny has 5 T-shirts. 2 T-shirts are blue and 3 T-shirts are white. What fraction of Manny's T-shirts are blue?

	Think	Write
Step 1:	Draw a picture that shows the total number of parts or pieces.	🎽 🎽 🎽 🎽 🎽
Step 2:	Decide what part of the picture you need to shade.	Two of the T-shirts are blue. I need to shade 2 T-shirts. 🎽 🎽 🎽 🎽 🎽
Step 3:	A. What's the numerator? What am I counting?	A. I am counting blue T-shirts. There are 2 blue T-shirts.
	B. What's the denominator? How many total parts/pieces are there?	B. There are 5 T-shirts in all. $\dfrac{\text{blue T-shirts} \rightarrow 2}{\text{all T-shirts} \rightarrow 5}$
	C. What is the answer?	C. Two-fifths of Manny's T-shirts are blue.

Practice Solving Math Problems

Directions Draw a picture and write a complete sentence to answer each question on a separate sheet of paper.

1. A pet store has 3 brown dogs and 4 black dogs. They get 2 more black dogs. What fraction of the dogs are black?

2. Gil has 2 green socks. Juana has 2 green socks and 6 pink socks. What fraction of Gil and Juana's total socks are green?

3. A garden has 3 red flowers, 2 green flowers, and 2 yellow flowers. What fraction of the flowers are NOT red?

4. Fabian cleaned 2 rooms of his house. He has 4 rooms left to clean. What fraction of his house has Fabian NOT cleaned?

Understand the Main Idea

Objective Show different ways to find fractions that name the same amount. Show different ways to compare and order fractions.

Learn the Main Idea

Are $\frac{1}{2}$ and $\frac{4}{8}$ equal to each other?

You can make a model to find out.

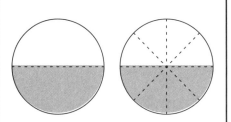

These fractions name the same amount: $\frac{1}{2} = \frac{4}{8}$

Is $\frac{1}{2}$ greater than $\frac{1}{3}$?

You can use a number line to find out.

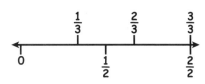

$\frac{1}{2}$ is to the right of $\frac{1}{3}$, so $\frac{1}{2}$ is greater than $\frac{1}{3}$.

You can also write this: $\frac{1}{2} > \frac{1}{3}$

How can you order fractions from least to greatest?

You can use fraction strips to find out.

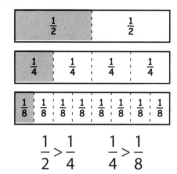

$\frac{1}{2} > \frac{1}{4}$ $\frac{1}{4} > \frac{1}{8}$

You can order the fractions from greatest to least: $\frac{1}{2}\ \frac{1}{4}\ \frac{1}{8}$

 MAIN IDEA There are different ways to find fractions that name the same amount. There are different ways to compare and order fractions.

Practice Applying the Main Idea

Directions: Look at the pictures at the start of every problem. Then use one of the following phrases to complete the sentences: *greater than, less than, the greatest, the least, the same amount.*

1

The first fraction names $\frac{1}{2}$. The second fraction names $\frac{2}{8}$. $\frac{1}{2}$ is _____ $\frac{2}{8}$.

2
This fraction names $\frac{1}{8}$. $\frac{1}{8}$ is _____.

3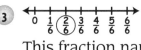
This fraction names $\frac{2}{6}$. $\frac{2}{6}$ is _____ $\frac{5}{6}$.

4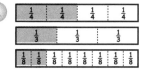

$\frac{2}{4}\ \frac{1}{3}\ \frac{2}{8}$ In what order are these fractions?

_____

Learn the Vocabulary

Objective Use the term *equivalent fraction* to talk about fractions that name the same amount.

Learn the Words

$\frac{1}{2}$ and $\frac{2}{4}$ are equivalent fractions because they name the same amount.

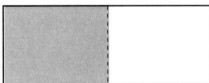

This picture shows the fraction $\frac{1}{2}$.

This picture shows the fraction $\frac{2}{4}$.

$\frac{2}{6}$ and $\frac{6}{12}$ are not equivalent fractions because they do not name the same amount.

This picture shows $\frac{2}{6}$.

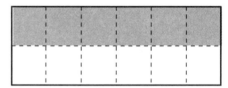

This picture shows $\frac{6}{12}$.

Practice the Words

Directions Look at the pictures, and write the fraction for each picture. Describe the fractions. Use a sentence with *because* to explain if they are equivalent fractions. Use a separate sheet of paper.

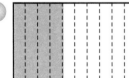
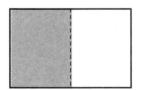
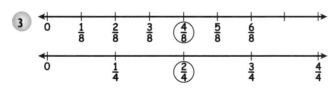

④ Draw a fraction strip and divide it into 6 equal parts. Shade 2 parts.

Draw another same-sized fraction strip underneath. Divide the fraction strip into 3 equal parts. Shade 1 part.

Write the fraction names for the shaded parts on each fraction strip.

Do the shaded parts on each fraction strip match? Why?

Use More Language

Objective Tell how to compare and order fractions using sentences
with the word *that*.

Learn the Language

 $\frac{4}{8}$  $\frac{3}{6}$

$\frac{4}{8}$ and $\frac{3}{6}$ are equivalent fractions that name
the amount of pizza we ate.

 $\frac{3}{4}$

The part of the circle that is shaded
is larger than the white part of the
circle. $\frac{3}{4}$ is a fraction that is greater
than $\frac{1}{4}$.

 $\frac{2}{3}$

The part of the circle that is shaded
is larger than the white part of the
circle. $\frac{2}{3}$ is a fraction that is greater
than $\frac{1}{3}$.

 $\frac{1}{2}$

The part of the circle that is shaded is
equal to the white part of the circle.
$\frac{1}{2}$ and $\frac{1}{2}$ are equivalent fractions.

$\frac{2}{3}$ is a fraction that is greater than $\frac{1}{2}$, but less than $\frac{3}{4}$. You can write these fractions in order from
least to greatest: $\frac{1}{2}$ $\frac{2}{3}$ $\frac{3}{4}$.

Practice the Language

Directions Compare the pictures and the fractions. Complete the sentences
using *that*.

Example

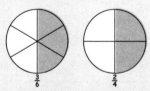 $\frac{3}{6}$ $\frac{2}{4}$

The parts of these circles ... that are
shaded show equivalent fractions. $\frac{3}{6}$ and $\frac{2}{4}$
are equivalent fractions.

1 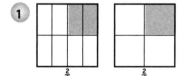 $\frac{2}{8}$ $\frac{2}{4}$

The parts of these squares ... _____

_____

2

The part of the circle ... _____

_____

3

$\frac{1}{2}$ is a fraction ... _____

_____

Solve Math Problems

Objective Decide what questions with *if* mean when solving word problems.

Learn to Solve Problems

Problem Diego ate $\frac{2}{3}$ of a pizza. If the pizza had 6 pieces, how many pieces did Diego eat?

	Think	Write
Step 1:	Read the problem. Underline the question. Decide what you need to find out.	"If" means we don't know for sure how many pieces the pizza had. We need to find out how many pieces of pizza Diego ate.
Step 2:	Circle the facts.	He ate $\frac{2}{3}$ of a pizza. Maybe there were 6 pieces of pizza.
Step 3:	Draw pictures, or use fraction strips or models. Solve the problem.	Diego ate $\frac{2}{3}$ of a pizza. I will draw a picture with 3 pieces and shade 2 parts. What part do I need to shade in for a pizza with 6 pieces to match $\frac{2}{3}$? I need to shade 4 pieces. Then the shaded parts of both pizzas will match. Diego ate 4 pieces of pizza.

Practice Solving Math Problems

Directions Follow steps 1 to 3 above to solve the word problems below. Solve the problems on a separate sheet of paper.

1. Ani made a loaf of bread and cut it into slices for her friends. She gave away $\frac{1}{2}$ of the bread. If the bread had 8 slices, how many slices did she have left for herself?

2. Gil had a slice of bread. He ate $\frac{2}{3}$ of the bread. If he cut the bread into 6 pieces, how many pieces did Gil eat?

3. Juan shared $\frac{1}{2}$ of his stickers with his friends. If he had 6 stickers, how many stickers did he share?

4. Gaia ate $\frac{4}{5}$ of a pizza. If the pizza had 10 pieces, how many pieces did he eat?

Understand the Main Idea

LESSON 1

Objective Write decimal numbers that show fractional parts of a whole.

Learn the Main Idea

 There are ten blocks. Three blocks are blue. The model shows that three of the ten blocks are blue.	$\frac{3}{10}$ ← There are three blue blocks. ← There are ten blocks in all. This fraction shows three tenths. Three tenths of the blocks are blue.	Ones | Tenths $\quad$ 0 . 3 ← $\quad$ 0.3 $\quad$ 0.3 is equal to $\frac{3}{10}$. This decimal number also shows three tenths. Three tenths of the blocks are blue.

Fractions and decimal numbers can be used to show the same parts of a whole.

MAIN IDEA You can use decimals to show fractional parts of a whole.

Practice Applying the Main Idea

Directions Write the decimal number that describes each picture. Then write a sentence about each decimal number. Use a separate sheet of paper for question 4.

Example

Write a decimal number for the blue pencils.

<u>0.3</u>   <u>Three tenths of the pencils are blue.</u>

①
Write a decimal for the blue stars.

___   _____

②
Write a decimal for the blue flowers.

___   _____

③
Write a decimal and a fraction to show the part that is colored. Why can you use both to show parts of a whole?

___   _____

④ Draw a collection of 10 stickers. Color 0.4 or $\frac{4}{10}$ to show the fractional part of a whole. Write a sentence to describe your picture.

Learn the Vocabulary

Objective Use vocabulary words that will help you talk and write about decimals.

Learn the Words

Directions Use the words on the left to fill in the blanks in the sentences on the right.

Ones	Tenths
0	.	4

$\dfrac{4}{10}$ four tenths

A **tenth** is 1 of 10 equal parts that make up a whole.

Ones	Tenths	Hundredths
0	.	3	8

$\dfrac{38}{100}$ thirty-eight hundredths

A **hundredth** is 1 of 100 equal parts that make up a whole.

0.38

A **decimal** is a number that shows parts of a whole. A **decimal point** is the dot that separates the ones from the tenths. The digits to the right of the decimal point show the parts of the whole.

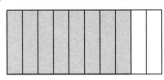

$\dfrac{8}{10} = 0.8$

eight _____

$\dfrac{56}{100} = 0.56$

fifty-six _____

The number 0.56 is a _____ number because the digits 5 and 6 are to the right of the _____.

Practice the Words

Directions Use the picture below to answer the questions. Use complete sentences.

1 What fraction of the squares are shaded?

_____

2 Write the fraction as a decimal number.

_____

3 In what place is the digit 7 in your decimal number?

_____

4 In what place is the digit 2?

_____

5 What do the digits to the right of the decimal point show? _____

_____

6 What are some ways that we use decimal numbers?

_____

_____

106 · Decimals

Use More Language

Objective Use the verbs *show* and *shade* to describe how to represent decimals.

Learn the Language

Ten objects are _____.
Five of the objects _____ are pens.
Three of the objects _____ are _____.
I need three _____ objects to _____ three tenths.

How many objects are shown?
How many of the objects **shown** are pens?
How many of the objects **shown** are **shaded**?
How many **shaded** objects do you need **to show** three tenths?

Practice the Language

Directions Use the picture of the muffin pan to answer questions 1 to 3. Use the picture of the grid to answer questions 4 and 5. Use a separate sheet of paper for the last question.

1. How many parts are shown?

_____

2. Write a fraction that shows the number of muffins that are left.

_____

3. Show $\frac{8}{10}$ as a decimal.

_____

4. How much of the grid is shaded?

_____

5. Show twenty-five hundredths as a fraction and as a decimal.

_____

6. Draw a picture to show 0.6. Write a question about the picture. Then write an answer. Use two of these words: *show, shown, shade, shaded.* Use complete sentences.

LESSON 4

Solve Math Problems

Objective Identify pronouns and what they mean in word problems.

Problem There are 10 boys on Hugo's soccer team. (They) buy a pizza and cut (it) into 10 equal parts. <u>Write a decimal to show how much of the pizza each boy gets.</u>

	Think	**Write**
Step 1:	Read the problem. Underline what you have to do.	I underlined what I have to do.
Step 2:	Circle the pronouns. Decide who or what each circled word means.	I circled the pronouns. I use <u>they</u> in place of the boys. So <u>they</u> means the boys. I use <u>it</u> in place of pizza. So <u>it</u> means pizza.
Step 3:	Solve the problem. Write the answer.	I need to write a decimal to show how much of the pizza each boy will get. There are 10 pieces in the pizza. There are 10 boys. Each boy will get 1 piece of pizza. Each boy gets 0.1 of the pizza.

Practice Solving Math Problems

Directions Read each problem below. Circle the pronouns. Write the answer to each step on a separate sheet of paper. Use complete sentences to answer each question.

1. Jee Woo has 10 stickers. She gives 3 of them to a friend. Write a decimal to show how many stickers she has left.

2. There are 10 horses in the field. Five of them are eating hay. Write a decimal to show how many of the horses are eating hay.

3. Luis has 100 baseball cards. He keeps 27 of them in a special book. Write a decimal to show how many of the cards are in the book.

4. Jia and Jose's family drink 10 glasses of orange juice every day. Jia and Jose each drink 3 glasses of it. Write a decimal to show how many glasses of orange juice they drink every day.

Understand the Main Idea

Objective Multiply and divide in your head by using patterns and basic facts.

Learn the Main Idea

I can use basic facts and patterns to multiply and divide in my head!

$3 \times 400 = 1,800 \div 2 =$

First, I will use a basic fact: $3 \times 4 = 12$.

Then I will use a pattern of zeros:

$3 \times 4 = 12$
$3 \times 40 = 120$
$3 \times 400 = 1,200$

The product has the same number of zeros as the factors.

First, I will use a basic fact: $18 \div 2 = 9$.

Then I will use a pattern of zeros:

$18 \div 2 = 9$
$180 \div 2 = 90$
$1,800 \div 2 = 900$

The quotient has the same number of zeros as the dividend.

> **MAIN IDEA** You can multiply and divide in your head by using patterns and basic facts.

Practice Applying the Main Idea

Directions Find the quotient or product in your head. On a separate sheet of paper, write the pattern for each problem. Then answer the last question on a separate sheet of paper.

Example $2 \times 400 = 2 \times 4 = 8; 2 \times 40 = 80; 2 \times 400 = 800$

1 $6 \times 300 =$

2 $4 \times 5,000 =$

3 $8 \times 7,000 =$

4 $560 \div 8 =$

5 $720 \div 9 =$

6 $2,400 \div 6 =$

7 Choose one multiplication problem or one division problem. Describe the pattern you used to do the problem in your head.

Learn the Vocabulary

Objective Use vocabulary words that will help you talk and write about multiplying and dividing in your head.

Learn the Words

Word/Phrase	Definition	Examples	
mental math	math you do in your head without using pencil and paper or a calculator	When I multiply 5 × 3,000 in my head, I am using mental math.	I can use mental math to divide: 4,500 ÷ 9 = 500.
basic facts	simple multiplication, division, addition, and subtraction facts	basic multiplication fact: 2 × 8 = 16	basic division fact: 15 ÷ 3 = 5
rule	the steps to follow to solve a problem	A multiplication rule: When I multiply by a multiple of 100, there will be 2 zeros in the product.	A division rule: When I divide, the number of zeros in the quotient equals the number of zeros in the dividend.
pattern	the order in which you do something over and over again	A multiplication pattern: 2 × 3 = 6 2 × 30 = 60 2 × 300 = 600	A division pattern: 18 ÷ 9 = 2 180 ÷ 9 = 20 1,800 ÷ 9 = 200

Practice the Words

Directions Read the two stories below. Fill in each blank with a vocabulary word or phrase from above.

Ahab doesn't have a pencil and paper to find the answer to 6 × 900. He wants to use _____ and do the math in his head. He knows a _____: 6 × 9 = 54. Ahab uses a _____ and adds two zeros to the product of the basic fact to get 6 × 900 = 5,400.

Luis doesn't want to use a rule, so he uses a basic fact: 6 × 9 = 54. Then he multiplies 6 × 90 = 540. Then he multiplies 6 × 900 = 5,400. Luis uses a _____ to get his answer.

Now show how you can use a pattern or a rule to find the answer for these number sentences. Use a separate sheet of paper.

1. 4 × 4,000 =

2. 3,600 ÷ 9 =

110 • Multiplication and Division Patterns in Mental Math

© Copyrighted Material – No Reproduction Permitted.

Use More Language

Objective Use sentences that begin with *if* to describe patterns and rules for multiplying and dividing in your head.

Learn the Language

If I multiply by a multiple of 10, 100, or 1,000, I can use a pattern.   **4 × 4,000 = ?**

The product has the same number of zeros as the factors.

$$4 \times 4 = 16$$
$$4 \times 40 = 160$$
$$4 \times 400 = 1{,}600$$
$$4 \times 4{,}000 = 16{,}000$$

If I divide a multiple of 10, 100, or 1,000, I can use a pattern.   **8,000 ÷ 4 = ?**

The quotient has the same number of zeros as the dividend.

$$8 \div 4 = 2$$
$$80 \div 4 = 20$$
$$800 \div 4 = 200$$
$$8{,}000 \div 4 = 2{,}000$$

REMEMBER: If the basic fact has a 0 in it, the product has 1 more 0 than the factors.
$$5 \times 4 = 20$$
$$5 \times 40 = 200$$

REMEMBER: If the basic fact has a 0 in it, the quotient has 1 fewer 0 than the dividend.
$$20 \div 4 = 5$$
$$200 \div 4 = 50$$

Practice the Language

Directions Use a rule or a pattern to find the answer to each number sentence. Then, on a separate sheet of paper, write a sentence with *if* to explain how you got your answers.

Multiplication

Example
$6 \times 4{,}000 =$ If I multiply by a multiple of 1,000, I will put 3 zeros in the product. $6 \times 4 = 24$; $6 \times 4{,}000 = 24{,}000$.

1 $6 \times 500 =$

2 $9 \times 9{,}000 =$

Division

Example
$4{,}000 \div 5 =$ If the basic fact has a zero in it, the quotient will have 1 less zero than the dividend. $4{,}000 \div 5 = 800$.

3 $1{,}000 \div 2 =$

4 $5{,}600 \div 7 =$

Solve Math Problems

Objective Decide what *a number* and *the number* mean in a word problem.

Learn to Solve Problems

Problem   When a number is (divided by 4), the (quotient is 6,000). What is the number?

Step 1:   Read the problem. Underline the question.

A number in the sentence is the same as **the number** in the question.

Step 2:   Circle the facts.

I circled the facts. "Divided by 4" means that 4 is the divisor. The quotient is 6,000. That means the answer is 6,000.

Step 3:   Write the number sentence to solve the problem.

The quotient is 6,000. _____ ÷ _____ = 6,000

Divided by 4 means that the divisor is 4.

_____ ÷ 4 = 6,000.

24 ÷ 4 = 6, so 24,000 ÷ 4 = 6,000. The dividend and the quotient have the same number of zeros.

 Practice Solving Math Problems

Directions Read each problem. Underline the question, and circle the facts. Then write a number sentence solving the problem. For question 4, write a complete explanation for each step and solve the problem on a separate sheet of paper.

Example   When a number is (divided by 7), the (quotient is 700). What is the number? 4,900 ÷ 7 = **700**

1. When a number is divided by 4, the quotient is 400. What is the number?

_____

2. When a number is multiplied by 6, the product is 42,000. What is the number?

_____

3. When a number is divided by 5, the quotient is 2,000. What is the number?

_____

4. When a number is multiplied by 9, the product is 8,100. What is the number?

Understand the Main Idea

Objective Describe ways to estimate products and quotients.

Learn the Main Idea

I can use rounding to estimate the product.

Estimate the product:
4 X 192

I will round 192 to the nearest hundred.

192 rounds to 200

4 × 192 is about 800.

4 × 200 = 800

4 × 192 is about 800

I can use compatible numbers to estimate the quotient.

Estimate the quotient:
47 ÷ 6

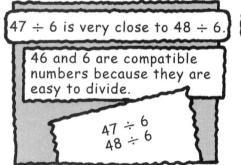

47 ÷ 6 is very close to 48 ÷ 6.

46 and 6 are compatible numbers because they are easy to divide.

47 ÷ 6
48 ÷ 6

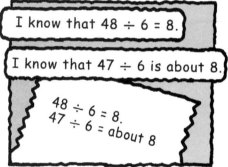

I know that 48 ÷ 6 = 8.

I know that 47 ÷ 6 is about 8.

48 ÷ 6 = 8.
47 ÷ 6 = about 8

MAIN IDEA You can estimate products and quotients in different ways.

Practice Applying the Main Idea

Directions Circle the correct word to complete the sentence.

1 When you multiply, you can use _____ to estimate.
rounding   triangles   square numbers

2 When you divide, you can use _____ to estimate.
weight   compatible numbers   data

3 One way to estimate a _____ is to use rounding.
bar graph   degrees Celsius   product

4 One way to estimate a _____ is to use compatible numbers.
polygon   quotient   fact family

5 Write a sentence describing how you can estimate a quotient.

_____

_____

Learn the Vocabulary

Objective Use vocabulary words that will help you estimate quotients.

Compatible numbers are numbers that are easy to divide.

The numbers in these problems are compatible numbers:

These are basic division facts.

The numbers are easy to divide.

You probably know that $64 \div 8 = 8$ and that $35 \div 7 = 5$.

The numbers in these problems are **not** compatible numbers:

These are **not** basic division facts.

These numbers are **not** easy to divide.

Most people do not know $37 \div 4$ or $49 \div 9$.

Directions Circle the division problem if the numbers are compatible numbers. Cross out the division problem if the numbers are NOT compatible. Write a sentence to explain how you know.

1 $16 \div 2$

_____

_____

_____

2 $38 \div 9$

_____

_____

3 $101 \div 5$

_____

_____

_____

4 $45 \div 9$

_____

_____

Use More Language

Objective Break apart long sentences to understand them better.

Learn the Language

These directions are long and confusing.

Estimate the product by rounding the factor greater than 10 to its greatest place.

Let's break the sentence apart so we can understand it better

<u>Estimate</u>	the <u>product</u>	by <u>rounding</u> the	<u>factor greater than 10</u>	to <u>its greatest place</u>.
What do I have to do?	*What will I estimate?*	*How will I estimate?*	*What will I round?*	*What will I round it to?*
I have to estimate.	I will estimate the product.	I will use _____.	I'll round the _____ _____.	I'll round it to its _____ _____.

Practice the Language

Directions Break apart each long sentence to help you understand the directions. Show your thinking by writing questions and answers on a separate sheet of paper. Answer the last sentence on this page.

1. Estimate to decide if each quotient is greater than 100 or less than 100.

2. Change the dividend to a number that can be easily divided by 5 and 10.

3. Write a multiplication problem with a product that is between 60 and 70.

4. Write a sentence to explain why it is a good idea to break apart long sentences.

_____

_____

_____

_____

Solve Math Problems

Objective Identify and solve multi-step problems.

Learn to Solve Problems

Problem Mihai drinks about 6 glasses of milk a week. Does he drink more or less than 200 glasses of milk in a year? (There are 52 weeks in a year.)

First: Read the problem. Underline the question.

Next: Circle the important facts.

Then: Identify the steps you need to solve.

First, I have to find about how many glasses of milk Mihai drinks in a year. I will use

estimation. Then, I have to compare that number to 200.

Last: Write number sentences. Then write a sentence to solve the problem.

$6 \times 50 = 300$

Mihai drinks about 300 glasses of milk in a year.

$300 > 200$

Mihai drinks more than 200 glasses of milk in a year.

 Practice Solving Math Problems

Directions Follow the steps above to solve the problems. Estimate products and quotients. Write number sentences for end part of the problems. Write complete sentences to solve the problems.

1. Ms. Saha parks her car in a 7-story parking garage. Each story holds 196 cars. When the garage is full, are there more than 2,000 cars or fewer than 2,000 cars parked in the garage?

2. Hugo has 211 stamps in his collection. He puts the stamps into 5 boxes with about the same number of stamps in each box. About how many stamps are in each box?

3. Marta buys 6 bracelets that are all the same price. She spends a total of $44.00. Does each bracelet cost more or less than $5.00?

4. A basketball team plays 5 games. The team scores 88 points in each of 2 games, and 61 points in each of the other 3 games. About how many points does the team score in all?

Understand the Main Idea

Objective Identify and count what is left over in a division problem.

Learn the Main Idea

1.
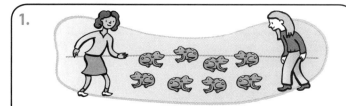
There are 8 frogs. There are 2 girls. Each girl gets an equal number of frogs.

2.

Each girl gets 4 frogs. There are no frogs left over.

3.
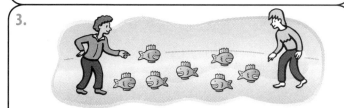
There are 7 fish. There are 2 boys. Each boy gets an equal number of fish.

4.

Each boy gets 3 fish. There is 1 fish left over.

 MAIN IDEA Sometimes when you divide, there is something left over.

Practice Applying the Main Idea

Directions Look at the pictures. Draw a line to connect each picture with the sentences that tell about it.

1

    a. There are 3 circles. Each circle has 3 marbles. There are 2 marbles left over.

2

    b. There are 2 circles. Each circle has 3 marbles. There is 1 marble left over.

3

    c. There are 3 circles. Each circle has 2 marbles. There are 0 marbles left over.

4 On a separate sheet of paper, write a few sentences that tell about the marbles in the picture on the right.

Learn the Vocabulary

Objective Talk and write about what is left over in a division problem, using the vocabulary word *remainder*.

Learn the Words

Problem Pedro has 17 blocks. He wants to build 3 towers. Each tower will have an equal number of blocks.

How many blocks will be in each tower? I need to divide 17 blocks into 3 towers to find out.

$$17 \div 3 = ?$$

Each tower has five blocks. But two blocks are left over. The blocks that are left over are the **remainder**. 17 divided by 3 is 5 with a remainder of 2.

$$17 \div 3 = 5 \quad R2$$

remainder

Practice the Words

Directions Color the cubes that are left over. Then count the cubes that are left over. Write the missing numbers or words in the blank.

1. The remainder is ____.

2. The remainder is ____.

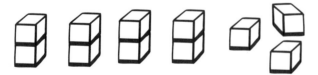

3. The _____ is 2.

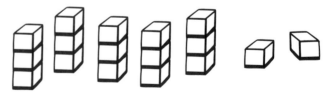

4. Choose one of the questions you solved. Write a sentence to explain how you found the remainder.

_____

_____

_____

Use More Language

Objective Use *if . . . then* statements and division vocabulary to tell when a division problem has a remainder.

LESSON 3

Learn the Language

When you divide, you can compare the number left over to the divisor to see if there is a remainder.

Example 1 7 ÷ 4 The divisor is 4. There are 3 left over. **If** the number left over is less than the divisor, **then** there is a remainder.	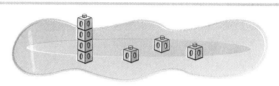 7 ÷ 4 = 1 R3
Example 2 6 ÷ 2 The divisor is 2. There are 0 left over. **If** the number left over is 0, **then** there is no remainder.	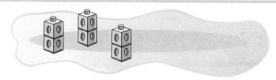 6 ÷ 2 = 3
Example 3 10 ÷ 3 The divisor is 3. There are 4 left over. Oops! That's a problem! **If** the number left over is greater than or equal to the divisor, **then** I need to try a larger quotient. I can make 3 towers with these cubes.	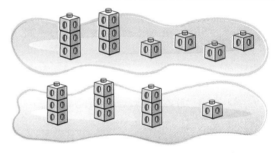 10 ÷ 3 = 3 R1

Practice the Language

Directions Complete the *if . . . then* statements so the sentences make sense.

1. If the number left over is greater than or equal to the divisor, then _____ _____.

2. If the number left over is 0, then _____ _____.

3. If _____, then it's a remainder.

4. If _____, then there is no remainder.

5. Write a sentence to explain how sentences 2 and 4 are alike.

_____

_____

_____.

Solve Math Problems

Objective Write the missing question when you know the answer to a problem.

Learn to Solve Problems

Problem Luz has 23 grapes and 3 plates. She puts 7 grapes on each plate. The answer is 2 grapes. Write the question.

Step 1: Read the problem. Underline what you have to do. Circle the facts.

Step 2: Use counters or drawings to model the problem.

Step 3: Write the sentence that tells what the answer is. The answer is 2 grapes.

Look at the counters. Find the group that represents the answer.

Step 4: Use one of these question frames to write the question.
How many _____ are there at the beginning?
How many equal groups of _____ are there?
How many _____ are there in each group?
How many _____ are left over?

How many grapes are left over? _____

Practice Solving Math Problems

Directions Follow steps 1 to 4 above to solve the word problems below. Show your work on a separate sheet of paper.

1 Sala has 19 buttons. She puts her buttons into equal groups with 6 buttons in each group. She has 1 button left over. Write the question.

2 Gil has 22 toy cars. He puts them in 4 equal rows. There are 2 cars left over. The answer is 5 cars. Write the question.

3 The students in Ms. Parr's class form 7 groups with 3 students in each group. There are no students left over. The answer is 21 students. Write the question.

4 Sam has 20 blocks and 4 shelves. He puts 5 blocks on each shelf. The answer is 0. Write the question.

MAIN IDEA A glossary is the part of a book where you find out what a word means.

How Do I Use a Glossary?

In a glossary, words are in alphabetical order, from A to Z, just like in the alphabet. **Pint** will come after words that start with N or O, but before words that start with Q or R.

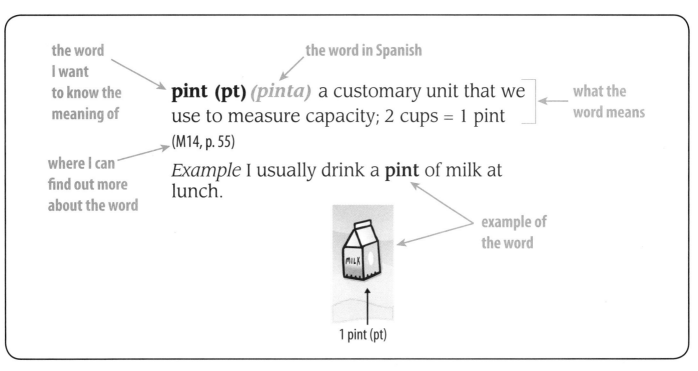

the word I want to know the meaning of

the word in Spanish

pint (pt) *(pinta)* a customary unit that we use to measure capacity; 2 cups = 1 pint (M14, p. 55)

what the word means

where I can find out more about the word

Example I usually drink a **pint** of milk at lunch.

example of the word

1 pint (pt)

GLOSSARY

A.M. *(A.M.)* the time of a day between midnight and noon (M15, p. 58)

Example School starts at 8:00 **A.M.**

about *(aproximadamente)* not the exact number, but close to that number (M3, p. 10)

Example A penny is **about** the same size as a dime.

acute angle *(ángulo agudo)* an angle that is smaller than a right angle (M20, p. 79)

acute triangle *(triángulo agudo)* a triangle with three acute angles (M21, p. 83)

addends *(sumandos)* numbers that you add in an addition problem (M5, p. 18)

Example 10 + 8 = 18
10 and 8 are **addends**.

angle *(ángulo)* two rays or line segments that come together at the same endpoint (M20, p. 78)

area *(área)* a measurement that shows how much space a plane figure covers (M24, p. 94)

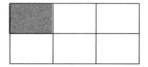

array *(coleccíon, ordenación)* a way to show items in rows and columns (M8, p. 30)

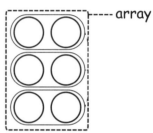

Associative or Grouping Property of Addition *(propiedad asociativa de la suma)* the rule that says you can group addends in different ways and still get the same answer (M5, p. 19)

Example 3 + (2+3) = 8
(3+2) + 3 = 8

basic facts *(operaciones básicas)* simple addition, subtraction, multiplication, and division facts (M28, p. 110)

Example 3 × 3 = 9
15 ÷ 5 = 3

bill *(billete)* a piece of paper money (M4, p. 14)

break apart *(descomponer)* to separate a number into two smaller numbers because the smaller numbers are easier to work with (M9, p. 34)

calendar *(calendario)* a chart that shows the days, weeks, and months of the year (M16, p. 62)

capacity *(capacidad)* the amount a container, such as a glass, can hold (M14, p. 54)

Example The **capacity** of this milk container is one gallon.

cent *(centavo)* a unit of money; 100 cents = 1 dollar (M4, p. 14)

centimeter (cm) *(centímetro)* a metric unit that we use to measure length or distance (M13, p. 51)

classify *(clasificar)* to group similar things together (M21, p. 81)

Example You can **classify** shapes in different ways. Some shapes are circles and some shapes are squares.

closed figure *(figura cerrada)* a plane figure that begins and ends at the same point (M21, p. 82)

coin *(moneda)* a flat, round piece of money made from metal (M4, p. 14)

Commutative or Order Property of Addition *(propiedad conmutativa de la suma)* the rule that says you can add two numbers in any order and still get the same sum (M5, p. 19)

Example 2 + 5 = 7
5 + 2 = 7

Commutative or Order Property of Multiplication *(propiedad conmutativa de la multiplicación)* the rule that says you can multiply two factors in any order and get the same product (M8, p. 30)

Example 3 × 2 = 6
2 × 3 = 6

compare *(comparar)* to show how two items are similar or different (M2, p. 6)

compatible numbers *(números compatibles)* numbers that are easy to add, subtract, multiply, or divide (M29, p. 114)

Example 25 × 4 = 100
10 ÷ 2 = 5

cone *(cono)* a solid figure with a circle as its base and a curved surface that meets at a point (M23, p. 91)

congruent *(congruente)* figures that have the same size and shape (M22, p. 86)

contain *(contener)* to hold something inside (M14, p. 54)

container *(recipiente)* an object, such as a box or bottle, that can hold something in it (M14, p. 54)

Example This **container** has grapes inside it.

cube *(cubo)* a solid figure that has six square faces (M23, p. 91)

cubic unit *(unidad cúbica)* the unit used when measuring the volume of an object (M24, p. 94)

cup (c) *(taza de medir)* a customary unit that we use to measure capacity or how much of something there is (M14, p. 55)

Example This container holds one **cup** of juice.

1 cup (c)

customary *(usual)* something that we do or use all the time; the system of measurement that is used in the U.S. (M13, p. 50)

Example Feet, yards, and inches are **customary** ways to measure length in the United States.

cylinder *(cilindro)* a solid figure with two circles as bases (M23, p. 91)

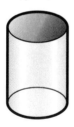

data *(datos)* information or facts (M18, p. 70)

date *(fecha)* a specific day, month, and year (M16, p. 62)

Example On July 20, 1969, Neil Armstrong became the first person to set foot on the moon.

decimal *(decimal)* a number that shows parts of a whole (M27, p. 106)

Example 0.50 is a **decimal** that shows half of one whole.

decimal point (.) *(punto decimal)* a dot that is used to show where whole dollars end and cents begin (M4, p. 14); the dot that separates ones from tenths in a decimal (M27, p. 106)

$$0.38$$

decimeter (dm) *(decímetro)* a metric unit that we use to measure distance or length; 10 centimeters = 1 decimeter (M13, p. 51)

degree (°) *(grado)* a unit used when measuring temperature (M17, p. 66); a unit used when measuring an angle (M20, p. 78)

Example Today it is 45 **degrees** outside. Right angles have a 90 **degree** angle.

degrees Celsius (°C) *(grados Celsius)* the metric units that we use to measure temperature (M17, p. 66)

degrees Fahrenheit (°F) *(grados Fahrenheit)* the customary units that we use to measure temperature (M17, p. 66)

denominator *(denominador)* the bottom part of a fraction; it shows the total number of equal parts (M25, p. 98)

$$\frac{3}{6} = \frac{\text{numerator}}{\text{denominator}}$$

digit *(dígito)* any one of the 10 symbols: 0, 1, 2, 3, 4, 5, 6, 7, 8, 9 (M1, p. 2)

Example In the number 32, 3 and 2 are the **digits**.

divided by *(dividido por)* the way we read the symbol ÷ (M10, p. 38)

Example 8 ÷ 4 = 2
8 **divided by** 4 equals 2.

dividend *(dividendo)* the total number of items that are divided by another number (M10, p. 38)

Example 8 ÷ 4 = 2
8 is the **dividend**.

division rules *(reglas de la división)* any number divided by one equals that number; any number divided by zero equals zero (M12, p. 46)

Example 8 ÷ 1 = 8
8 ÷ 0 = 0

divisor *(divisor)* the number used to divide the dividend (M10, p. 38)

Example 8 ÷ 4 = 2
4 is the **divisor**.

dollar *(dólar)* a unit of money that is worth 100 cents (M4, p. 14)

doubling/doubles *(duplicar/dobles)* adding a number to itself (M9, p. 34)

Example 2 + 2

edge *(arista)* the line segment that is formed where two faces meet (M23, p. 90)

edge

elapsed time *(tiempo transcurrido)* the amount of time between the start and the end of an activity (M15, p. 58)

Example The **elapsed time** between 8:30 and 9:00 is 30 minutes.

endpoint *(extremo)* the point at either end of a line segment or the point at one end of a ray (M20, p. 78)

enough *(suficiente)* sufficient; as many numbers or things as I need (M7, p. 26)

Example A sticker costs 25 cents. I have 15 cents. I do not have **enough** money to buy the sticker.

equal groups *(grupos iguales)* groups that have the same number of items (M8, p. 30)

Example There are four **equal groups** of cherries.

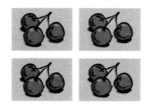

equal parts *(partes iguales)* pieces of a whole that are all the same size (M25, p. 98)

equal to (=) *(igual a)* when something is the same as something else (M2, p. 6)

Example $1.00 is **equal to** four quarters.

equilateral triangle *(triángulo equilátero)* a triangle with all sides the same length (M21, p. 83)

equivalent fraction *(fracción equivalente)* fractions that name the same amount (M26, p. 102)

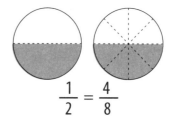

$$\frac{1}{2} = \frac{4}{8}$$

estimate *(estimación)* an approximate number that is close to the exact amount (M6, p. 22)

Example 13 + 29 is about 40.
40 is an **estimate**.

exact answer *(respuesta exacta)* the actual sum, difference, product, or quotient (M6, p. 22)

Example 13 + 29 = 42
42 is the **exact answer**.

face *(cara)* the flat surface of a solid figure (M23, p. 90)

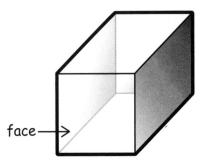

face →

fact family *(familia de operaciones)* number sentences in addition and subtraction, or multiplication and division that use the same numbers (M5, p. 18)

Example 4 + 3 = 7   7 − 3 = 4
3 + 4 = 7   7 − 4 = 3

factor *(factor)* a number that you multiply by another number to get an answer (M8, p. 30)

Example 5 × 4 = 20
5 and 4 are **factors**

flip *(invertir, reflejar)* to turn something over (M22, p. 87)

foot (ft) *(pie)* a customary unit that we use to measure length or distance; 12 inches = 1 foot (M13, p. 51)

Example A ruler is one **foot** long.

fraction *(fracción)* a number that can describe a part of a whole or part of a group or set of things (M25, p. 98)

Example The **fraction** $\frac{3}{6}$ shows one-half of the pie.

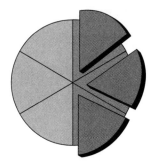

gallon (gal) *(galón)* a customary unit that we use to measure capacity; 4 quarts = 1 gallon (M14, p. 55)

gram (g) *(gramo)* a metric unit that we use to find out how heavy an object is (M14, p. 55)

Example This paper clip weighs about 1 **gram**.

1 gram (g)

graph *(gráphico/a)* a chart or diagram that uses pictures, bars, or lines to show information (M19, p. 74)

greater than (>) *(mayor que)* when something is bigger, longer, or taller than something else (M2, p. 6)

Example The number 82 is **greater than** the number 9.

group/set *(grupo/conjunto)* a number of things that go together (M25, p. 98)

halfway between *(en el punto medio entre)* in the middle of two things or numbers (M3, p. 10)

Example The number 5 is **halfway between** 1 and 10.

1   5   10

hexagon *(hexágono)* a polygon with six sides (M21, p. 83)

hundreths *(centésimos)* 1 of 100 equal parts that make up a whole (M27, p. 106)

Identity or Zero Property of Addition *(propiedad de identidad de la suma)* the rule that says when you add zero to any number, the answer is always that number (M5, p. 19)

Example 8 + 0 = 8
9 + 0 = 9

Identity Property of Multiplication *(propiedad de identidad de la multiplicación)* the rule that says when any number is multiplied by 1, the answer is always that number (M9, p. 34)

Example $4 \times 1 = 4$
$8 \times 1 = 8$

inch (in) *(pulgada)* a customary unit that we use to measure length or width (M13, p. 51)

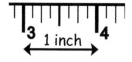

increase *(aumentar)* to become greater or larger (M3, p. 10)

intersecting lines *(rectas secantes)* lines that cross (M20, p. 79)

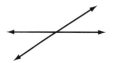

inverse operation *(operaciones inversas)* number sentences that are the opposite of each other, such as addition and subtraction (M5, p. 18)

Example 12 + 6 = 18 is the **inverse operation** of 18 − 6 = 12.

isosceles triangle *(triángulo isósceles)* a triangle with two sides that are the same length (M21, p. 83)

key *(clave)* an explanation of what the symbols in a pictograph mean and how much or how many each symbol stands for (M19, p. 74)

Example The **key** in a graph tells what each symbol stands for.

kilogram (kg) *(kilogramo)* a metric unit that we use to measure mass; 1,000 grams = 1 kilogram (M14, p. 55)

Example I bought two **kilograms** of apples.

1 kilogram (kg)

kilometer (km) *(kilómetro)* a metric unit that we use to measure distance or length; 1,000 meters = 1 kilometer (M13, p. 51)

label *(letrero)* words that tell what kind of data is in a graph (M19, p. 74)

less than (<) *(menor que, menos que)* when something is smaller or shorter than something else (M2, p. 6)

Example The height of the mouse is **less than** the height of the elephant.

line *(recta)* a straight path that goes in both directions without endpoints (M20, p. 78)

line of symmetry *(eje de simetría)* an imaginary line that goes down the middle of a figure; if you fold the figure on the line, both sides match (M22, p. 86)

line plot *(diagrama lineal)* a diagram that sorts data on a number line (M18, p. 70)

```
        X       X
    X   X   X   X           X
  ──────────────────────────────
    4   5   6   7   8   9
        Number of People
```

line segment *(segmento de recta)* a part of a line (M20, p. 79)

liter (L) *(litro)* a metric unit that we use to measure capacity; 1,000 milliliters = 1 liter (M14, p.55)

Example I have one **liter** of water for the recipe.

1 liter (l)

M

mass *(masa)* in the metric system, how heavy something or somebody is (M14, p. 54)

Example The **mass** of these grapes is 10 grams.

measure *(medir)* to find out how big something is or how much of something there is (M13, p. 50)

mental math *(cálculo mental)* math you do in your head without the help of a pencil, paper, or calculator (M28, p. 110)

meter (m) *(metro)* a metric unit that we use to measure distance or length; 100 centimeters = 1 meter (M13, p. 51)

metric *(métrico/a)* a system of measurement based on tens (M13, p. 50)

Example Meters and centimeters are used to measure length in the **metric** system.

mile *(milla)* a customary unit that we use to measure length or distance; 5,280 feet = 1 mile (M13, p. 52)

milliliter (mL) *(mililitro)* a metric unit that we use to measure capacity (M14, p. 55)

Example An eyedropper holds about one **milliliter** of water.

1 milliliter (ml)

mode *(moda)* the number in the data that you see most often (M18, p. 70)

multiplication table *(tabla de multiplicación)* a chart that shows multiplication facts (M12, p. 46)

	1	2	3	4
1	1	2	3	4
2	2	4	6	8

number *(número)* a symbol that is made up of digits, often used for counting (M1, p. 2)

Example 43 and 569 are **numbers**.

numerator *(numerador)* the top part of a fraction; it shows the number of parts you are counting (M25, p. 98)

$$\frac{3}{6} = \frac{\text{numerator}}{\text{denominator}}$$

obtuse angle *(ángulo obtuso)* an angle that is larger than a right angle (M20, p. 79)

obtuse triangle *(triángulo obtuso)* a triangle that has one obtuse angle (M21, p. 83)

octagon *(octágono)* a polygon with eight sides (M21, p. 83)

open figure *(figura abierta)* a plane figure that is not complete; not all of its sides are connected (M21, p. 82)

opposite *(opuesto)* things that are very different from each other (M11, p. 42)

Example Addition is the **opposite** of subtraction.

order *(ordenar)* to arrange things so you can compare them or learn how they are the same or different (M2, p. 6)

ordinal numbers *(números ordinales)* numbers that show position or order (M16, p. 62)

Example First (1ˢᵗ), second (2ⁿᵈ), third (3ʳᵈ), and fourth (4ᵗʰ) are **ordinal numbers**.

ounce (oz) *(onza)* a customary unit that we use to measure weight (M14, p. 55)

P.M. *(P.M.)* the time of the day between noon and midnight (M15, p. 58)

Example I go to bed at 8:30 P.M.

parallel lines *(líneas paralelas)* lines that never cross and are always the same distance apart (M20, p. 79)

parallelogram *(paralelogramo)* a quadrilateral that has two pairs of equal sides that are parallel (M21, p. 83)

pattern *(patrón)* numbers or things that follow a certain order so you can tell what comes next (M9, p. 34); the order in which you do something over and over again (M28, p. 110)

Example: A, B, C, A, B, C, ___, B, C
The missing letter in the **pattern** is A.

pentagon *(pentágono)* a polygon with five sides (M21, p. 83)

perimeter *(perímetro)* a measurement used to show the distance around a plane figure (M24, p. 94)

Example The ant walked around the **perimeter** of the square.

perpendicular lines *(rectas perpendiculares)* lines that cross and form right angles (M20, p. 79)

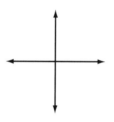

pint (pt) *(pinta)* a customary unit that we use to measure capacity; 2 cups = 1 pint (M14, p. 55)

Example I usually drink a **pint** of milk at lunch.

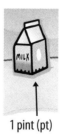

1 pint (pt)

place *(posición)* the location of a digit in a number (M1, p. 2)

Example The digit 4 is in the ones **place** in the number 94.

place value *(valor posiciónal)* the value we give to the place where a digit is in a number (M1, p. 2)

plane figure *(figura plana)* a figure that is flat like a sheet of paper (M21, p. 82)

point *(punto)* an exact position (M20, p. 79)

polygon *(polígono)* a closed figure with three or more straight sides (M21, p. 82)

pound (lb) *(libra)* a customary unit that we use to measure weight; 16 ounces = 1 pound (M14, p. 55)

Example The cheese weighs one **pound**.

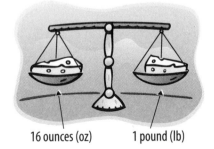

16 ounces (oz)   1 pound (lb)

product *(producto)* the answer to a multiplication problem (M8, p. 30)

Example $5 \times 6 = 30$

30 is the **product**.

property *(propiedad)* a rule that is always true and helps you know how to add or multiply (M5, p. 18)

Example The Order **Property**, Grouping **Property**, and Zero **Property** are all **properties** of addition.

pyramid *(pirámide)* a solid figure with a polygon as the base and triangles that share one vertex as faces (M23, p. 91)

quadrilateral *(cuadrilátero)* a polygon with four sides (M21, p. 83)

quart (qt) *(cuarto de galón)* a customary unit that is used to measure capacity; 2 pints = 1 quart (M14, p. 55)

Example My mother bought a **quart** of milk at the store for our family.

1 quart (qt)

quotient *(cociente)* the answer in a division problem (M10, p. 38)

Example 8 ÷ 4 = 2

2 is the **quotient**.

range *(rango)* the difference between the greatest and least number in a set of data (M18, p. 70)

Example The **range** between the numbers 25 and 30 is 5.

ray *(rayo)* a part of a straight line that has one endpoint (M20, p. 79)

reasonable *(razonable)* an answer that makes sense (M6, p. 22)

Example 40 is a **reasonable** estimate for 13 + 29.

rectangle *(rectángulo)* a quadrilateral with four right angles (M21, p. 83)

rectangular prism *(prisma rectangular)* a solid figure with rectangular faces (M23, p. 91)

Example A **rectangular prism** is shaped like a shoebox.

regroup *(reagrupar)* to trade; to exchange equal amounts; to rename numbers (M7, p. 26)

related fact *(operación relacionada)* facts that use the same numbers (M11, p. 42)

Example Fact families show **related facts**, such as: 3 × 7 = 21; 21 ÷ 7 = 3.

remainder (R) *(residuo)* what is left over in a division problem (M30, p. 118)

Example 17 ÷ 8 = 2 **R1**

repeated addition *(suma repetida)* adding the same number more than two times (M8, p. 30)

Example 3 + 3 + 3

repeated subtraction *(resta repetida)* subtracting the same number until the answer is zero (M10, p. 38)

Example 8 ÷ 4 = 2

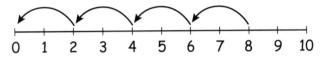

rhombus *(rombo)* a quadrilateral that has four equal sides and two pairs of parallel sides (M21, p. 83)

right angle *(ángulo recto)* an angle that measures 90 degrees (M20, p. 79)

right triangle *(triángulo rectángulo)* a triangle that has one right angle (M21, p. 83)

round *(redondear)* to change a number to another number that is close, but is easier to work with (M3, p. 10)

Example You can **round** 285 to 300.

rounding place *(lugar de redondeo)* the value of the number you round to (M3, p. 10)

Example When you round 230 to the nearest hundred, the hundreds place (2̲00) is the **rounding place**.

rule *(regla)* the steps you follow to solve a problem (M28, p. 110)

scale *(escala)* the numbers on a thermometer that measure temperature (M17, p. 66)

scalene triangle *(triángulo escaleno)* a triangle with no sides the same length (M21, p. 83)

separate *(separar)* to put into different places or different groups (M10, p. 38)

share equally *(compartir igualmente)* to put the same number of items in each group (M10, p. 38)

similar *(similar)* figures that have the same shape; they can be the same size or different sizes (M22, p. 86)

skip counting *(contar de __ a __)* counting from one number to another, not counting the numbers in between (M9, p. 34)

Example 2, 4, 6, 8, 10 is **skip counting** by 2s.

slide *(deslizar, trasladar)* to move from side to side, up or down, or sideways (M22, p. 87)

solid figure *(figura sólida)* a geometric figure with length, width, and height (M23, p. 90)

Example A cube is a **solid figure**.

sphere *(esfera)* a solid figure that is shaped like a ball (M23, p. 91)

square unit *(unidad cuadrada)* a unit used when measuring area (M24, p. 94)

square *(cuadrado)* a quadrilateral with four equal sides and four right angles (M21, p. 83)

standard *(estándar)* a way to measure that never changes and is the same for everyone (M13, p. 50)

Example A yard is a **standard** way to measure length.

sum *(suma)* the answer in an addition problem (M5, p. 18)

Example 6 + 6 = 12

12 is the **sum**.

survey *(encuesta)* to get information by asking people questions (M18, p. 70)

symbol *(símbolo)* a sign that represents something else; a picture that represents data in a pictograph (M19, p. 74)

Example The book **symbol** in the graph shows how many books the girl read.

symmetric *(simétrico/a)* a figure that has two halves that match exactly (M22, p.86)

tally chart/tally table *(tabla de conteo)* a way to show data using tally marks (M18, p. 70)

4	||
5	|
6	||
7	|

tell time *(decir la hora)* to find out what time it is, using a clock (M15, p. 58)

Example Look at the clock to **tell time**.

temperature *(temperatura)* how hot or cold something is (M17, p. 66)

Example The **temperature** today is 70 degrees. It is hot.

tenths *(décimos)* 1 of 10 equal parts that make up a whole (M27, p. 106)

thermometer *(termómetro)* a tool we use to measure the temperature (M17, p. 66)

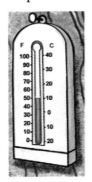

title *(título)* the name that describes what something is (M19, p. 74)

trapezoid *(trapecio)* a quadrilateral with exactly one pair of parallel sides (M21, p. 83)

triangle *(triángulo)* a polygon with three sides (M21, p. 83)

turn *(girar, rotar)* to move around a point (M22, p. 87)

unit *(unidad)* a certain quantity that we use to measure things (M13, p. 50)

Example There are many different **units** to measure length.

value *(valor)* how much a digit is worth in a number (M1, p. 2)

Example The **value** of 5 in the number 50 is tens.

vertex/vertices *(vértice/ vértices)* a point where three or more edges meet on a solid figure (M23, p. 90); a point where two rays of an angle meet

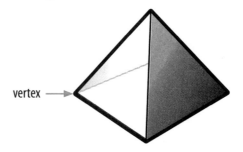

vertex

volume *(volumen)* a way to measure how much space is inside a solid figure (M24, p. 93)

weight *(peso)* in the customary system, how heavy something or somebody is (M14, p. 54)

Example The **weight** of the box of pasta is one pound.

whole *(entero/a)* all of a thing or of a group of objects (M25, p. 98)

yard (yd) *(yarda)* a customary unit that we use to measure length or distance; 3 feet = 1 yard (M13, p. 51)

Example A soccer field is 70 **yards** wide and 110 **yards** long.

Zero Property of Multiplication *(propiedad de cero de multiplicación)* the rule that says anytime you multiply a number by zero, the answer is always zero (M9, p. 34)

Example $9 \times 0 = 0$
$7 \times 0 = 0$

SPANISH COGNATES

Some of the math words you know in Spanish can help you learn math words in English. Look at the list below to find out what words you already know in both languages.

English	Spanish
angle	*ángulo*
area	*área*
calendar	*calendario*
capacity	*capacidad*
Celcius	*Celsius*
centimeter	*centímetro*
circle	*círculo*
cone	*cono*
congruent	*congruente*
cube	*cubo*
cylinder	*cilindro*
decimal	*decimal*
decimeter	*decímetro*
denominator	*denominador*
difference	*diferencia*
digit	*dígito*
divide	*dividir*
dollar	*dólar*
double	*doble*
equation	*ecuación*
equivalent	*equivalente*
estimate	*estimar*
factor	*factor*
Fahrenheit	*Fahrenheit*
figure	*figura*
fraction	*fracción*
gallon	*galón*
gram	*gramo*
graph	*graphico/a*
hexagon	*hexágono*
kilogram	*kilogramo*

English	Spanish
kilometer	*kilómetro*
line segment	*segmento de línea*
liter	*litro*
meter	*metro*
mixed number	*número mixto*
multiplication	*multiplicación*
numerator	*numerador*
octagon	*octágono*
order	*orden*
ounce	*onza*
parallelogram	*paralelogramo*
pentagon	*pentágono*
perimeter	*perímetro*
pint	*pinta*
plane	*plano*
point	*punto*
polygon	*polígono*
prism	*prisma*
product	*producto*
quotient	*cociente*
ray	*rayo*
rectangle	*rectángulo*
regroup	*reagrupar*
rhombus	*rombo*
similar	*similar*
solid	*sólida*
sum	*suma*
order	*ordenar*
triangle	*triángulo*
volume	*volumen*
yard	*yarda*